MW00627289

The New Science of UFOs

New insights into an old mystery

Eric Haseltine PhD   Chris Gilbert MD PhD

Discovery Democracy Press

Published in the United States by Discovery Democracy Press

The New Science of UFOs
New insights into an old mystery

Copyright © 2024 by Eric Haseltine and Chris Gilbert
All rights reserved.

Published 2024

ISBN: 978-0-9981228-3-0: Paperback

ISBN: 978-0-9981228-4-7: E-Book

Other books by Eric Haseltine

Long Fuse Big Bang

Brain Safari

The Spy in Moscow Station

Other books by Chris Gilbert

The French Stethoscope

Dr. Chris's ABC's of Health

Other books by Eric Haseltine and Chris Gilbert

The Listening Cure

Riding the Monster

Imagination is more important than knowledge.

Albert Einstein

To be able to ask a question clearly is two-thirds of the way to getting it answered.

John Ruskin

Forward

A completely fresh look at the UFO mystery

This book offers novel ideas about how to unravel the UFO mystery, a mystery which both the Pentagon and NASA said in recent reports is vital for US National security.

By "fresh ideas," we mean that we present a different, potentially more robust approach to exploring UFOs (or Unexplained Anomalous Phenomena–UAP if you prefer) than the data-driven approach the Government and others have taken, where they seek to solve the mystery by collecting more detailed information, deploying more "persistent surveillance" sensors, interviewing more witnesses, etc.

But will more information get us there?

Despite thousands of witness reports over 80+ years, video and film recordings, radar data, and infrared data from military sensors, we seem no closer to answers than when pilots first reported seeing flying saucers in the 1940s. We've gotten more data (including information that the Government has never disclosed), but that added data hasn't produced important new insights if we are to believe Government witnesses and reports. So, is even *more* data needed, or something else?

It could be something else.

Although science does inch forward by gathering new data to get new answers, science makes *quantum leaps* when it asks new *questions*.

Consider the centuries-long mystery of the cause of infectious disease. Medical science struggled for many decades to get their heads around it, despite evaluating multiple theories (the most popular being vaporous Miasmas) and despite gathering crucial data such as the 1676 discovery of bacteria and Ignaz Semmelweis's discovery in 1850's that some "particles" caused childbed fever (sepsis following childbirth). Scientists in the mid-1800s simply were unable to connect the dots linking bacteria to disease, not because they didn't have enough data, but because they didn't ask the right questions or thought they already had the answers (Medical colleagues of Semmelweis, certain Miasmas were the answer, locked Semmelweis away in an insane asylum, where he died of abuse for questioning "the truth")

It wasn't until the end of the 1800s that scientists such as Pasteur and Koch had the imagination to ask the right question: is an infectious disease caused by microorganisms, not malodorous "miasmas?" After asking that question, scientists such as Louis Pasteur finally gained insight into the root cause of contagious diseases.

We suspect that today, as with the infectious disease mystery, answers to the UFO mystery are not forthcoming, not necessarily due to a lack of data but because we aren't asking the right questions.

What if, for instance, as with infectious diseases, the answers stare us right in the face, but we don't know what we're looking at, and we lack the *point of view* to "connect the dots?" Or are we looking for crucial new information in the wrong places and requiring a complete shift in our point of view to start looking in the *right* places?

We use the phrase "point of view" here because Turing award winner Alan Kay observes that "Point of view is worth 80 IQ points."

Pasteur and Koch made giant scientific leaps by shifting their scientific *point of view* to see the problem from a completely different perspective.

And that's what this book will do: offer completely different points of view for looking at the data we already have on UFOs and suggest completely new places to look for data that we don't have but need to solve the riddle.

A sneak peek of what's inside

Here's a sneak peek of this approach, explained in more detail later in the book.

The most startling aspect of UFO reporting is the astonishing, seemingly effortless accelerations that UFOs achieve without moving parts and without spewing any heat, jet or rocket exhaust, or producing sonic booms from faster-than-sound travel.

What kind of propulsion system could do that? Indeed, none that we know of, even in the drawing-board stage. Thus, NASA and other Government scientists studying UFOs are looking into exotic propulsion systems such as Ion drives, nuclear propulsion, and other advanced concepts.

But what if these scientists and engineers look in the wrong place because they ask the wrong question: "What kind of propulsion plant could do that?"

Shifting point of view on ultrafast accelerations, what if a more insightful question is: what does fundamental physics -not aeronautical engineering– tell us about how to achieve jaw-dropping accelerations?

Well, physics says that when something accelerates that fast, it's because either an overwhelmingly powerful force moves it or it has extremely low mass (or both), allowing it to move quickly without prodigious amounts of force.

So, a better question than What kind of onboard propulsion plant could do that? Is: How low of *a mass* could those things have?

This leads to another fresh question: What if these things have very low mass *and no onboard propulsion* but are pushed or pulled from external forces such as directed energy beams? (For example, NASA has done this in the lab with NASA's "laser tweezers" that move things around with powerful beams of light).

Or an even more radical question: What if the phenomena have *no mass whatsoever* but are some optical projections akin to a laser light show in the night sky? "Objects" with zero or near zero mass (such as free air plasmas) can zip around with arbitrarily fast accelerations and, incidentally, *produce no sonic booms!*

Another unique question this book asks is What if someone, with the skills of an illusionist, is intentionally faking the seemingly impossible performance of UFOs to mess with our heads?

This book is also different in that it dares to try to imagine previously unimaginable answers to the UFO mystery. We undertake this seemingly impossible task because nothing guarantees that humans are smart enough, experienced enough, or imaginative enough to comprehend what's happening with UFOs, just as prehistoric humans would be unable to get their heads around how an iPhone works.

If UFOs are to us what iPhones would be to cave dwellers, we'll only get closer to the truth by traveling right up to the limits of our imaginations and beyond. Possibly, far beyond, as you'll see with some of the radically new ideas we'll surface.

You can sense where this book comes from now: Whether asking new questions such as those focused on mass will get us to the ultimate answer (or answers) is unknown, but adding new, sometimes radical points of view can't hurt.

Which is why we title this book *The New Science of UFOs.* Yes, we will dive into cutting-edge astrophysics, exotic propulsion, astrobiology, and other new scientific discoveries that could shed light on the mystery. However, by "new," we also mean new points of view. We'll surface novel perspectives on what ETs might be like if they're behind the mystery and original thinking about their motivations.

Paying homage to Alan Kay's wisdom about the value of point of view, we hope to up your UFO IQ by 80 points.

Eric Haseltine PhD   Chris Gilbert MD PhD

Table of contents

Introduction

An exciting science mystery

Issac Asimov, a Ph.D. Biochemist and Science fiction writer quipped, *The Most Exciting Phrase in Science Is Not 'Eureka!' But 'That's Funny'*

Recent congressional testimony from Naval aviators, the Pentagon's establishment of a new organization to understand UAPs (the new term for UFOs), and a 2023 NASA report on UAPs all strongly suggest that science is experiencing a "That's funny" moment with UFOs right now.

That is to say, a few of the many thousands of reported UFO sightings, such as those by Navy aviators, are real; not necessarily ETs, but unexplained, nevertheless.

Such mysteries are Nature's way of whispering, "Look closer; there's something new and fundamental you can learn about how I work."

Over our long careers in science and medicine, we have both experienced sparkly bubbles in our upper abdomens when hearing Nature whisper this way, and both of us are feeling those special tingles right now about UFO reports.

A genuine scientific mystery in the skies is unfolding, pulling, enticing, and exciting us to uncover clues that take us closer to the truth.

And that mystery is vibrant with many layers and nuances.

On the surface, the science mystery is how UFOs move in the many astonishing ways that have been reported by military pilots and other highly credible witnesses in the last 20 years, including hovering, abrupt mid-air braking, turning on a dime, changing altitude at jaw-dropping speeds and even vanishing into thin air.

But even more scientifically mysterious than what UFOs do is what they *don't* do.

In none of the sightings deemed to be both valid and unexplained in recent DOD and NASA UAP reports do the craft–if that's what they were-show any apparent means of propulsion such as propellers, jet engines, rockets, nor any of the standard flight control surfaces such as ailerons, flaps or rudders.

Exhaust plumes, heat discharges, vapor trails, or even signs of exotic drives–such as ion engines–that emit light or luminous plasmas were similarly absent, ditto air intakes and exhaust or vectored thrust nozzle.

Oh, and several reported UFOs, like the ones those Naval aviators reported near San Diego, appeared to go supersonic while causing no sonic boom. Supersonic flight can occur without big booms on the ground if the aircraft has the right shape (like a thin needle), but the "objects" in question don't have those shapes. Check out the shape of this one photographed from an F/A-18 cockpit over the Pacific. (1)

Credit: US NAVY

Yes, about 30% of UFOs reported were either streaking or floating balls of light or otherwise associated with lights of some sort, hinting at propulsion mechanisms that emit light (more about that later). Still, most reports are more noteworthy for what they didn't cover than what they did cover. (1,2)

Many credible and unexplained sightings are of objects straight out of science fiction movies, describing craft with apparent anti-gravity levitation and propulsion systems without visible moving parts, exhaust, etc.

For example, on Nov 14, 2004, near San Diego, multiple Navy personnel, including aviators and shipborne radar operators, filed consistent reports that included visual, video, infrared, and radar data of truly astonishing flight patterns, including dropping from low Earth orbit to 80,000 feet in seconds, abruptly changing directions, and disappearing instantaneously "as if shot out of a gun." Analysis of the sensor recordings (2) and eyewitness reports estimated the G forces (accelerations) of the fighter jet-sized Tic Tac-looking objects ranged from about 70 Gs to over 5000 Gs. (1,2,3,4,5,6).

The Tic Tacs seemed smooth with no moving parts, engines, or flight control surfaces and emitted no exhaust, heat plumes, or light, causing no sonic booms and, remarkably, when flying close to the ocean surface, no disturbance in the water. (1,2,3,4,5,6)

Here is an Infrared frame capture of one of the multiple Tic Tac shapes reported that day.

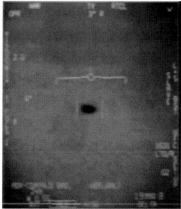

Credit: US NAVY

For reference, the most advanced air-to-air missiles sometimes experience up to 100 Gs, but 1000 Gs would tear them apart. If you crashed into a concrete wall going 60 MPH, and you had a crumple zone that brought you to a complete stop in 75 milliseconds, you'd experience a paltry -36 Gs of deceleration.

Even if such reports aren't due to exotic craft of human—or non-human manufacture, if you still believe that the "credible" reporters in question were sincere—questions of what kind of optical illusions or weird atmospheric effects—of the kind that could also produce video, infrared and radar anomalies—might cause the apparitions are scientifically interesting, falling squarely into Asimov's "That's funny" zone.

Let's consider optical illusions, which might explain other sightings for which we only have eyewitness accounts (these constitute most reports). In the next chapter, where we start our quest for the truth by examining the validity of human observation, we'll suggest why some of the reports might arise from errors in cognition, judgment, and perception based on a large body of knowledge of human perception and cognition. For instance, we'll describe the autokinetic illusion that makes stationary lights appear to dance around erratically in the night sky, like some UFOs.

But as large as that body of information is, it's still small relative to everything yet to be discovered about the human brain. Could some reports derive from optical illusions or other brain quirks that have yet to be discovered? Given that new optical illusions are being discovered all the time, like the one below where the blurry center appears to move when you slowly sweep your eyes across it, that's a distinct possibility.

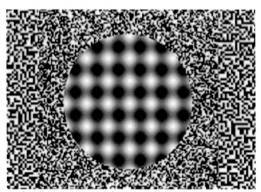

Credit: zaphad 1, CCA2.0 Wikimedia Commons

So, even if UFOs don't represent mysterious technology, they may still reveal new mysteries about the brain, not just mysteries of visual perception but of judgment, cognition, and motivation.

Or, supposing that neither exotic propulsion nor human perceptual/cognitive errors can explain UFOs (or at least some of them), the search for the cause of UFOs could lead to a deeper understanding of strange atmospheric phenomena.

As with optical illusions, previously unknown meteorological phenomena are being uncovered all the time, such as STEVE (Strong Thermal Emission Velocity Enhancement), which is caused by interactions between the Earth's ionosphere and magnetosphere that emit eerie lights resembling the aurora borealis (northern lights) but in much more southern latitudes. (7)

Credit Elfiehall CC BY-SA 4.0 Wikimedia Commons

It's unlikely that we've already discovered everything there is to know about our atmosphere, ionosphere, and magnetosphere, so it's not unreasonable to suppose that UFOs are Nature's way of whispering to us, "Look more closely at your atmosphere."

Considering the wide variety of credible UFO reports, and looking at the complex interplay of human perception, atmospheric effects, and flying objects, it seems likely that UFOs aren't one mystery but multiple mysteries that may or may not be connected.

What if multiple unrelated actors, multiple illusions, and/or multiple weird atmospheric effects underlie the wide variations in UFO reports?

So, we invite you to join us as sleuths and come along on this science journey as we turn the lens of hard science on the UFO question, surfacing and then evaluating hypotheses about the multiple truths that could be behind the phenomena.

Our first step in this journey, Chapter 1, is to calibrate the primary instrument for gathering data about UFOs: the human brain. What are the limitations, biases, motivations, and blind spots of this instrument? Where can we trust it, and where should we have a healthy skepticism about what it's reporting?

And the most intriguing question is, "How can we overcome our brain's limitations to imagine the unimaginable?" What if a few of the UFO sightings are to our brains what smartphones would be to our hunter-gatherer ancestors? Do we have the experience or knowledge to piece together what we were seeing? Is it possible to imagine the unimaginable? Read the chapter and see!

Next, we'll examine the mystery of how UFOs move with what appear to be astonishing accelerations. We'll look at ultra-advanced propulsion systems that NASA and others are exploring, including ion drives, energy beams, and other exotic means of propulsion that the known laws of physics dictate are possible. These include the possibility that the UFO "objects" are not physical objects in the sense of a craft of some sort, but low-to-zero mass optical phenomena formed from high-energy beams.

Having explored the art of known propulsion physics, we'll then tackle unknown, but not impossible propulsion physics such as warp drives, levitation, Mach effect drives, and yes, wormhole travel.

Acknowledging that some–if not all–of the unexplained sightings might be natural, instead of human or ET-made, we'll turn next to exotic meteorological and atmospheric possibilities such as ball lightning, sprites, cosmic rays, weird light refraction and diffraction, moon dogs, sun dogs, air plasmas and other physical forms of luminescence.

Then, we'll have some fun describing how someone could have faked at least some of the UFOs, not with doctored photos (as has been done many times), but with honest-to-God life-sized aerial apparitions that, in real-time, would look like and behave like some of the more perplexing UFOs. Here, we'll borrow our long experience faking things at Disney Imagineering, our knowledge of optics, and the neuroscience of magic tricks. We'll also look at why someone might *want* to pull off such elaborate, expensive fakery on a grand scale, resurrecting some military history on deception, ferret operations, intimidation, and diversionary tactics that could be highly relevant.

The last two chapters critically examine the hypothesis that UFOs are *unnatural* flying phenomena (instead of clever magic tricks) originating from human or non-human intelligence.

Could the most credible sightings, occurring as they do around military flight ranges, come from human adversaries who have unexpected breakthroughs in propulsion? Is one part of the US Government secretly messing with the heads of another part of the Government? Or buckle your seatbelts for this one–is it theoretically possible that UFOs have their origins in human activity in the future, reflecting somehow into the present, or even from intelligent entities from Earth's far distant past? Physics offers tantalizing hints, via weird properties of special relativity (time dilation) and quantum mechanics (entanglement, quantum erasers), that such extraordinary ideas, although highly unlikely, are not impossible.

You might question why two self-described hard scientists could bring up time travel (or warp drives or other exotica, for that matter). The answer is that, before the fact, the ultimate truth underlying most science mysteries almost always sounds far-fetched and foolish, such as continental drift, the asteroid extinction of dinosaurs, the bacterial origin of ulcers, and quantum superposition (quantum entities are in multiple places at the same time).

As Sherlock Holmes observed, whatever remains, however improbable, must be the truth when you've eliminated the impossible.

You'll hear us emphasize this theme of low-probability ideas ultimately proving true throughout the book as a constant reminder that, in all probability, the ultimate truth probably lives in the land of low probability.

This brings us to the last chapter on the intelligent non-human origins of UFOs. Suppose scientists someday rule out –or at least can ascribe vanishingly low probabilities to every human or natural origin for the most credible UFO reports? What does that leave?
By the Holmesian process of elimination that takes us to intelligent, but non-human possibilities.

We'll start with some fundamental astrobiology, revealing the latest scientific theories on the origins of life on Earth, including the panspermia hypothesis that life came to Earth from space.

What have we learned about extremophiles (that can survive the vacuum of space, extreme heat, and extreme cold) that could inform the possibility of unearthly life forms? Has astronomy –using spectrographic analysis of the atmospheres of exoplanets-found hints of life elsewhere in our galaxy?

References

1) https://www.aaro.mil/Portals/136/PDFs/UAP_Reporting_Trends_as_of_20Nov23.pdf?ver=dl2m2HXgCl-MaJ9t5wBmk9Q%3d%3d

2) https://www.archives.gov/news/topics/ufo

3) https://docs.house.gov/meatings/IG/IG05/20220517/114761/HHRG-117-IG05-Transcript-20220517.pdf

4) https://www.armed-services.senate.gov/imo/media/doc/23-31_04-19-2023.pdf

5) https://www.dni.gov/files/ODNI/documents/assessments/FY2023-Consolidated-Annual-Report-UAP-Oct2023.pdf

6) https://smd-cms.nasa.gov/wp-content/uploads/2023/09/uap-inde-pendent-study-team-final-report.pdf

7) American Geophysical Union (Aug 20, 2018). "New kind of aurora is not an aurora at all ."*Physorg.com*. Retrieved 2018-08-21.

1. The brain's perception of UFOs

We'll illustrate why we begin with the human dimension of UFOs with a personal story.

Page Arizona, 1997

Lying on the warm, red desert sand, gazing up at the stars in the crystal-clear night, I (Eric) watched satellites in low Earth orbit swiftly transit above me—objects that looked like stars but weren't—following predictable, straight trajectories unlike the flash of meteors and decidedly faster than the ultraslow movement of stars with the Earth's rotation.

Then, my heart skipped a beat as one of the satellites, at least that's what I thought it was, made an abrupt right-angle turn, roughly two degrees of visual angle (the width of my thumb at arm's length), shifting its trajectory and then proceeding straight again towards the far horizon.

My scientist's brain tried to make sense of what I'd just seen, calculating that the G forces of making such a startling change in direction would have torn any artificial satellite to pieces (moving laterally about 7 miles in a small fraction of a second) if, indeed, human technology could devise a propulsion system capable of causing such a move in low Earth orbit in the first place.

Had I just seen a UFO? Was it artificial, some unknown natural phenomena, or something not of this world?

Was I crazy, or what?

Why the story points us first to the brain

Almost all credible UFO reports, even the ones with photographic or radar evidence, start with a human observing something extraordinary in the sky, such as the Page Arizona incident.

But looking more closely at the extraordinary behavior of the flying object shows why we may not need to look further than human cognition, perception, and motivation to explain many, if not all, of the reports.

We start with my brain's assumption that I was looking at a satellite traversing the heavens. Sure, it followed exactly the type of trajectory of other satellites, with the same size and appearance, but was it a satellite?

Or did my brain do what human brains always do, according to Neuroscientist Michael Gazzaniga, and automatically and unconsciously craft a coherent story in real time to make sense of the information streaming into it, a logical story, but one that was wrong?

Like all good stories, the "story" my brain swiftly wove together had a beginning, middle, and end. The all-important beginning, which set the stage and context, was that satellites were transiting the night sky. In the middle, a new satellite appeared, and the end, naturally, was that the satellite behaved in a very un-satellite manner, jinking a degree or two before resuming its course.

But left to its own devices, my brain could easily have turned non-fiction (satellites were moving above) into fiction (one satellite made an impossible maneuver) by falling prey to an optical illusion.

What if, for instance, my brain, having just seen other satellites, believed it was seeing yet another orbiting body when, in fact, it was seeing a low-flying drone moving in the same direction as true satellites and at the same angular velocity?

Then, although the sensory input would have been identical to the first story, everything about the story would have been different if it had begun this way: A drone with a white light, flying a few hundred feet above the ground in a straight westward path, made a fast, but very drone-like rapid maneuver.

In the second story, there was no UFO, just a high-performance drone.

How many other UFO stories are products of distance/motion illusions, where someone's brain assumed a flying object was far away, in which case large movements of visual angle would be truly astonishing, when in fact the object was much closer so that large movements in apparent visual angle represented modest movements in time and space?

If you're having trouble grasping the concept of visual angle and distance/velocity confusion, imagine you are tossing a Frisbee around with friends in an open field.

If the Frisbee flies in front of you a few feet away, it will move across your visual field briskly. But the same Frisbee, flying a hundred feet from you, although traveling the same *linear* velocity (feet per second) as the one close to you, would have a much, much lower *angular velocity* (degrees of visual angle per second) with respect to a fixed line of sight.

Now imagine that you were standing in that same open field, not playing Frisbee or seeing anyone else playing Frisbee, and a Frisbee flew by you a few feet away.

Lacking context (e.g., I'm playing Frisbee golf with friends), your brain might wrongly assume the flying object was much further away than it was, in which case the flying disc would not only appear to be moving breathtakingly fast but would also appear to the way larger than it was because objects occupying the same visual angle will be perceived as having vastly different linear sizes based on their perceived distance from the eye (the Moon looks bigger on the horizon because the brain, seeing all the intervening terrain, perceives it as further away than when it's floating in an empty sky).

Here's an even more startling example of a size/distance illusion, where your brain mistakes a man standing atop a hill hundreds of yards from the tower for a giant standing right next to the tower.

Credit: Sureshforiphone CCA-Share Alike 3.0 Wikimedia Commons

In the image below, the photographer faked a UFO, by exploiting size/distance confusion.

Credit: Richard Elzey CC 2.0 Wikimedia Commons

The small flying disc is between the camera and the trees, but the eye could easily mistake the object for something larger flying beyond the trees.

The brain can also be fooled by size/distance/velocity illusions when interpreting electronic information.

This still frame is from a Naval F/A-18 fighter Infrared camera of a UAP (black dot) zipping across the ocean at a prodigious apparent speed.

Credit: US NAVY

But when NASA analyzed all the pertinent data, including the calculated altitude of the object (about 13,000 feet), speed of the F/A-18, the rate of movement of the infrared camera gimbal (moving mirrors that kept the sensor locked on the target), and speed and direction of the local wind, they concluded that the object was only traveling about 30-40 MPH, about the same speed as the wind at that altitude. (1)

All consistent with the mysterious object being a balloon.

Are UFOs like magic?

All magic tricks get our brains to tell fictional but perceived-to-be-true stories by carefully setting the stage for the all-important context setting at the story's start.

Consider the woman-sawed-in-half magic trick. The magician recruits your brain as an ally by telling you how the story begins: that they intend to cut the woman on the table into two pieces as they point to the hapless assistant lying on a table to reinforce their point. The woman may squirm or look fearful to bring the message home forcefully.

When the magician makes good on his threat, your brain completes the story the magician started, seeing the women's upper and lower halves apart. It's magic!!

How different a story your brain would have told you if the saga began: Two women wearing identical clothes are crammed uncomfortably contorted into two separate hollow platforms, made to look like a single regular table, such that you see only the top half of the first woman and bottom half of the other.

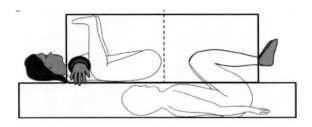

The story and your perception of what happened would have been vastly different.

Context is all-important in human perception, especially in UFO sightings.

The possibility that the equivalent of a magic trick could explain UFO behavior, whether perpetrated by mother nature, through meteorological phenomena, or some human mischief, gets stronger when you consider that, like magic tricks, UFOs sometimes do the impossible. And if a UFO seems to do the impossible, maybe what it's doing —such as moving at supersonic speeds with no sonic booms or without heat exhaust— *is* impossible, and something akin to a magic trick is happening.

What if, for instance, it was possible to project the equivalent of a neon sign in the sky, where the neon sign shows an animation of a moving, glowing disc?

Look closely at the sign below. Notice the faint outline of multiple unlit bowling balls? Also, looking closely, you can see unlit outlines of bowling pins on the sign's far left. When the different bowling balls turn on and off, starting from the right of the sign to left of the sign, a single ball appears to move continuously from right to left, "striking" the three pins on the left and causing the individual pins to wobble. The sequence of four images shows the progression of the "movement" of the bowling ball towards the pins.

Time

Credit: Andre Carrotflower CCA-Share Alike 4.0 Wikimedia Commons

So, what are entirely separate objects appear to be single, continuously moving objects. It's magic!

Could this be done with UFO-like objects, creating the illusion of ultrafast motion of a single object?

Let's examine one of the most compelling and unexplained series of UFO reports, those reported by the military near San Diego in 2004.

In that series of reports, flyers reported flying objects zooming from the upper atmosphere to the sea surface in mere seconds, traveling far faster than the speed of sound, yet producing no sonic booms and no visible form of exhaust or heat plume.

The first potentially faulty assumption that the Naval aviators might have made here is that the objects they saw were, in fact, objects.

Having spent so much time flying objects themselves and seeing countless other flying objects, the aviators could automatically and unconsciously perceive that an unnatural looking...well...*thing* moving about in the sky was a physical, self-powered object. In other words, the context setting the stage for the reports was that when pilots see something flying that isn't a bird, it must be an artificial object.

But what if the flying objects weren't objects at all? If they obeyed the known laws of physics, their extraordinary movements (assuming there was no velocity/distance confusion) would follow the equation $F=MA$. Rearranging this equation, we get $A=F/M$, where the acceleration (A) equals the force (F) applied divided by the mass (M), such that the astonishing A observed would have required exceptional F or zero or near zero M.

How can a flying "object" have zero mass?

Well, the Navy itself might have provided an answer in a (curiously) unclassified patent for a method of fooling enemy air-to-air missile seekers into tracking ghost airplanes (rather than the real thing) by projecting moving images of airplanes into the air, using high power lasers.

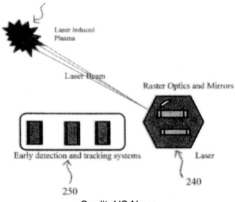

Credit: US Navy

Such lasers, shown below in an artist's concept (laser beam deflected with mirror), strip electrons from air molecules to create plasmas that are like 3-dimensional pixels, which, like pixels in a display, can be shaped and formed into images, like those of fighter airplanes. The laser-induced plasmas in the air can move instantaneously when fast-moving mirrors steer the laser beam in arbitrary directions. More about this in our chapter on faking UFOs. (2)

Plasma images are not precisely 3D holograms but have the same visual effect. Interestingly, such plasmas emit heat and reflect radar waves, so images of aircraft drawn with plasma pixels would also show up on thermal cameras and radars (the way the Navy-reported UFOs did).

The plasma theory, in which an unseen laser formed the images from some distance away to mess with the aviators' heads (for whatever reason), would also explain why no one heard sonic booms despite the faster-than-sound movement of the "objects." Perhaps the aviators reported no booms because no aerodynamic surfaces were present to displace air molecules.

It would be possible, with steered laser plasmas described in the Navy patent, to project the equivalent of a floating neon sign in the sky, where multiple plasmas, ignited along a flight path in an on-off sequence, could create the powerful illusion of a single object moving in "impossible ways." Perceptual psychologists and neuroscientists call such "apparent motion" the *Phi phenomenon,* which makes motion pictures and videos work, not by showing continuous action but by displaying a series of fast-changing still frames.

There's no direct evidence that artificial plasmas or the Phi phenomenon are responsible for UFOs. Still, you can see why understanding the human brain is crucial to understanding UFO sightings. The most important scientific instrument for gathering data on UFOs, the human brain, has inherent flaws, starting with its tendency to report erroneous data when fed the wrong initial context.

The change in official nomenclature from UFOs to Unexplained Anomalous Phenomena or UAPs (even though normal humans, like us, still call them UFOs) acknowledges the importance of context, removing the assumption that UFOs are 'flying' or 'objects' (but leaving the 'U' part).

One reason this change in terminology is so significant is that the reframing gets people to shift their focus solely from flying craft doing impossible things to other phenomena (such as natural ball lighting or unnatural laser plasmas) doing astonishing but entirely possible things (we'll stick with UFOs because everyone gets what those are).

The bottom line is if you see something doing the impossible, then the overwhelming odds are that you're not seeing what you *think* you're seeing.

Other illusions

Size, distance, and velocity judgment errors born of the wrong context aren't the only optical illusions that might account for some UFO reports. Here are a few others.

<u>Autokinesis</u>

If you go out on a clear moonless night and look at Venus or Jupiter, at some point, the glowing planets will appear to dance around erratically, not much, but enough to see, as suggested by the arrows.

Autokinesis is worth considering as an explanation of some of the baffling UFO movements, given that, according to a Pentagon-sponsored report (project Blue Book), about one-fifth of all UFO reports are misidentifications of astronomical phenomena such as stars, planets, and comets.

Here are some other examples of illusions that make things that aren't real appear real.

<u>Subjective contours</u>

 Below, there is no square; your brain fills in the straight lines. Thus, some of the reported weird shapes (Tic Tac, Triangles, etc.) may or may not have those shapes, even as evidenced in videos (the brain interprets those videos, after all).

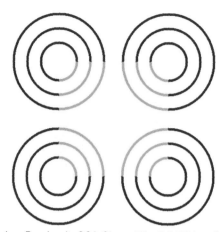

Credit Jochen Burghardt. CCA-Share Alike 3.0 Wikimedia Commons

Motion After Effects

Have you ever looked out the aircraft window while taxiing into the gate and realized the scenery is still moving even though the aircraft has stopped?

Credit Jules Verne Times Two CCA Wikimedia Commons

If so, you've experienced the fatigue of visual motion sensors for motion in one direction that let motion sensors in the opposite direction take over, creating the illusion of movement in the direction opposite your original movement. Pilots zipping over the ground, ocean, or among the clouds are subject to such motion aftereffects, and such artifacts may have influenced some of the sightings.

Vection

The inverse of motion aftereffect is *vection*, which is the mistaken sense that you are moving, when you are stationary, when something, like a train on the track next to you, moves, you have the illusion of moving in the opposite direction. This illusion arises from the powerful effect motion in your peripheral vision has on making you think you are moving. Again, pilots reporting UFOs have many opportunities for experiencing vection, especially near the ground or clouds, which could distort their perceptions of motion.

Credit Beau Wade Creative Commons Attribution 2.0 Wikimedia Commons

Reafference failure

Place your finger on the outer edge of one eye, then very gently nudge that eye towards your nose, as in the photo below. You will see the world jump in the opposite direction that you pushed on your eye because you don't ever perceive motion directly. Instead, you perceive the difference between the motion on the retina of your eye and the motion that the brain *expects to* see (this is called reafference). When you displace your eye, your brain does not command eye motion in the expected way (eye muscle movement). Therefore, when your brain detects movement of imagery on your retina, it assumes, incorrectly, that the world, not your retina, is moving. A pilot jostling around in turbulence and seat vibration transmitted to the head and eye could perceive something to be moving in erratic ways when it is not moving at all.

Even though illusions such as we've just described may or may not underlie some UFO reports, they bring home an uncomfortable truth: we do not perceive reality but actively construct it inside our heads in ways that can produce substantial errors.

This means that, as scientists evaluating the strengths and shortcomings of our instrument (the brain), we must go to great lengths to rule out perceptual and cognitive errors as causes of the phenomena we are studying.

Given that we need our admittedly faulty brains to rule out errors of those same brains, the task is indeed daunting.

When the brain doesn't understand what it doesn't understand

You can be forgiven for thinking we are pooh-poohing the possibility that at least some UFOs have an exotic origin, dismissing the reports as optical illusions, cognitive biases, or some other human shortcoming. And your impression that we are being unfairly dismissive could grow in later chapters as we explore atmospheric effects, fakery, etc.

But we aren't pooh-poohing anything. And we especially aren't invalidating the reports of UFOs, or the people who made the reports, or the people who believe UFOs exist or are of extraterrestrial origin. We are simply taking the first step that all scientists must take in doing their utmost to ensure they collect valid data and analyze it objectively.

A second step that scientists must take is to acknowledge their own biases, many of which are unconscious. In our cases, both of us, at an emotional level, want ETs to be a reality and secretly hope that someday, some UFOs will arise from alien origins because the idea of ETs excites our imaginations and curiosity. But knowing that's what we want deep down makes us critically question our interpretations and conclusions very closely at every step so that we ultimately don't get to what we *want* to be true but what is true.

But acknowledging bias isn't enough. In "calibrating our instrument" (the human brain), we must also acknowledge what that instrument is unable to collect, just as an optical telescope can't pick up radio waves, gravitational waves, infrared, or gamma rays, all of which carry critical astronomical data that are as, or more important for understanding the universe as visible band data.

And it is nearly certain that, like an optical telescope, the human brain is incapable of "collecting," let alone understanding everything there is to collect and comprehend about UFOs.

Nobel laureate Werner Heisenberg, Quantum Mechanics pioneer, summed it up nicely by observing, "Not only is the Universe stranger than we think, it is stranger than we *can* think."

When we asked Marvin Minsky, father of AI, about this, he responded, "That's right, my cat is the smartest cat I've ever met or even heard of, but I'll never teach it French."

So, what if we are the equivalent of intelligent cats and UFOs are the equivalent of French? A cat hears French and probably–if raised in France-knows a few French words and a fair amount of intonation, but it could never get its feline head around Voltaire, Descartes, or Sartre.

So, too, we can see and sense specific characteristics of UFOs with radar and infrared and understand some things about what we're seeing. Still, it's entirely possible, even likely, there's a lot we're missing.

For instance, we now know that there's a fair amount of astrophysics that we don't understand, such as the true nature of dark energy and dark matter, which together, if estimates are correct, make up about 95% of everything in the universe. But dark matter and energy are "known unknowns." A couple hundred years ago, no one suspected that dark matter and energy even existed, so all that dark stuff was then in the "Unknown unknown" category.

Like dark matter and dark energy were a hundred years ago, are there still more unknown unknowns lurking out there right now?

Most scientists would say that's a virtual certainty.

All of this means that, in approaching the mystery of UFOs, we must keep in the back of our heads the probability that there is nothing *in* those heads capable of wrapping those heads around the phenomena.

That doesn't mean that all is lost, however. Sometimes, when scientists can't directly see something, they define its boundaries not by what it is but by what it is *not*.

One example is how scientists use statistics not to prove a hypothesis but to *disprove* (or assign a very low probability) competing incompatible hypotheses. You've seen this if you've ever read a science paper in which statistics appeared with notations such as "$P<.01$" meaning, the probability that the null hypothesis (no experimental effect of a science manipulation) is less than one in a hundred, very strongly implying (but not proving) that the scientific manipulation (like giving a drug and seeing if it cures a disease) produces the hypothesized effect.

Perhaps a more straightforward way of grasping how it's possible to understand what you don't understand or see hints of the outline of such phenomena is by use of what artists call "negative space."

Here's an example: Suppose we were intelligent sea creatures who wanted to map out our environment (the world's oceans). We'd come up with something like this image, where black denoted all the bodies of water on the planet.

Credit Ethanjc7 Creative Commons Attribution-Share Alike 4.0 Wikimedia Commons

By defining elements of the environment, we can see, we have simultaneously defined what we *cannot* directly see (land).

In the same way, a novel way to tackle the UFO mystery might be to define aspects of the problem by what they are *not*. For instance, let's use negative space to generate hypotheses about the motivations of such ETs for visiting Earth.

Exploring the motivations behind whoever is behind UFOs

It seems logical that if UFOs are products of someone's intelligence (human or not), then understanding *why* those someones are doing what they're doing might go a long way towards giving us a point of view on *what* is going on. For example, suppose UFOs are science probes gathering data. In that case, the flashes of light that accompany many sightings might have something to do with that science mission, like stimulating optical responses of atmospheric molecules (the way we do with some kinds of molecular spectroscopy). On the other hand, if UFOs have a military purpose, such as intimidation, the same flashes of light might be a way of scaring us or of probing the reactions of our military.

In other words, the why (if there is a why) matters a lot as to the *what* of UFOs.

Science fiction writers and UFO enthusiasts have long attributed possible extraterrestrial visits here to human-like motivations such as the naked desire for conquest, a search for scarce resources, or scientific curiosity. Some have even attributed extraterrestrials' possible presence to altruistic motives, such as saving humans from themselves. These are all reasons *we* might explore other planets and civilizations, and some or all of them might prove to be correct,

But new insights about extraterrestrials and us are unlikely to emerge from such old ideas. To develop truly novel ideas, a novel approach is needed. As we said in the Forward, a *new point of view* is required.

One such approach, growing out of the artists' idea of negative space, is *anti-anthropocentrism*, in which we posit intelligent life forms who are explicitly *unlike* us and, therefore, likely to have motivations we would struggle to understand.

Human motivations stem from our desire to reproduce and our need to survive to do so. Other drives, such as bonding with other humans, territoriality, aggression, curiosity, and novelty seeking, all support our essential biological imperative to survive, thrive, and reproduce.

Imagine intelligent organisms that do *not:*

- Sexually reproduce (some earthly vertebrates reproduce without sex)
- Have scarce resources engendering aggression and conflict within or across species
- Emotionally bond with others of their species (orangutans, spiders, and other animals don't)
- Have curiosity and novelty-seeking behaviors (which help humans find new resources)

- Have finite lifespans (some earthly species, such as hydra, might be *immortal*)
- Require food or water to survive (for example, what if extra-terrestrials are formed of dark matter drawing life from dark energy, and UFOs are technologies that bridge the gap between ordinary matter and dark matter?)
- Derive from animal forms, but do they derive from other life forms such as plants (in which case extraterrestrial UFOs could, essentially, be types of spores or pollen) and harvest *food* from sunlight?
- Have written or spoken language or any other form of symbolic communication?
- Derive directly from biology but are hyper-advanced digital AIs created by distant biological entities.

We could go on, but you get the point. Imagining motivations and predicting behaviors of intelligent entities, who are wildly different from us and who, for reasons of their own, have traveled here—either themselves or through probes—would be exceedingly tricky.

But as noted above, except dark-matter-based life forms that consume dark energy (we threw that in to illustrate the radical ideas that extreme anti-anthropocentrism stimulates), examples of most other "alien" forms exist here on Earth. Explicitly, non-human motivations are not only possible but probable if alien life has anywhere near the diversity of life on Earth.

Negative space and the instrument of the human brain

Michelangelo said that he did not carve statues in marble, but instead, removed pieces of marble that *weren't* the statue, which already lived inside the marble before any chisel struck it.

That approach suggests a point of view to keep in mind that can help us with critical unknown unknowns that would otherwise escape us.

The truth about UFOs, as the X-files famously observed, is out there, but maybe the best or only way to ultimately see it is to chip away at things that aren't the truth until, like a masterpiece of sculpture, the hard truth slowly emerges from the hard rock concealing it.

Here's an example: We'll soon dive into the question of whether human adversaries (e.g., Russia or China) could have leaped ahead of the US in advanced propulsion systems and might have deployed such systems around our military flight ranges to gather intelligence or to generally mess with the heads of the US military (or both).

If this analysis ultimately ascribes a very low probability to the foreign adversary hypothesis and an equally low probability to any other human source of the phenomena (such as one part of the military messing with another part), then, following the scientific method of "proving" hypotheses by assigning very low (e.g., P<.01) probability to competing hypotheses, we can conclude, with some justification, that UFOs arise from non-human sources—even when our limited (cat --learning --French) brains might be incapable of fully imagining what those sources might be.

Summary

Summing up the importance of starting the search for answers to the UFO mystery by examining the mysteries of the human brain: although the truth might be "out there," paradoxically, the best place to start looking for it might not be "out there," but "in there," "there" being human perception, imagination and, above all, fresh human points of view on potentially non-human phenomena. Thus, as you consume what follows, keep one eye on the ideas and information we are going to feed your hungry brain and the other eye on that brain itself.

References

1) https://smd-cms.nasa.gov/wp-content/uploads/2023/09/uap-independent-study-team-final-report.pdf

2) System and Method for Laser Induced Plasma for Infrared Homing Missile Countermeasures US Patent application 20200041236 A1, 2020-02-06

2.   Exotic propulsion that's theoretically possible

Two shocking possibilities for aerospace propulsion arise when looking at UAP reports.

The first, if the phenomena are physical objects, is that it might be possible to push or pull flying objects way faster than we currently know how to do.

The second, if the objects do not originate on Earth, is that traveling vast distances through interstellar space is more practical than we thought.

Inherent in both possibilities lurks another one: that the laws of physics aren't what we think they are. For instance, contrary to Einstein, faster-than-light travel (or its equivalent, stay-tuned) might be doable to enable interstellar travel, maybe through wormholes or warp drives, both of which some physicists believe aren't yet proven to be *impossible* under the right conditions.

We'll return to the possibilities for exotic propulsion that emerge from exotic physics later, but for now, let's stick to known physics to explore the strange doings above our heads. We're diving into the magic of rocket science now so that later in the chapter, we can use that knowledge to explore two crucial questions: how might UFOs zip around like that, and precisely *who* might be doing that zipping around?

You don't have to be a rocket scientist to grasp rocket science

We can't say this section isn't rocket science because it is.

But we're going to bring the subject down to Earth, as it were so that non-scientists can understand what must be true if truly exotic propulsion is at play with UAPs.

When we say down-to-earth, we mean down to sea because we will explain the physics of propulsion with an intuitive model, the way boats move through the water.

Whether moving through air, land, sea, or space, the principles all boil down to one of two means of motion: to be pushed or pulled by an *external* force, like the sailboat on the left, or to be propelled from an *internal* force, such as the engine of this jet ski.

Returning to our rearranged equation A=F/M, whenever you see astonishing A (such as UAPs zipping around), it must be that either F (force) is enormous, that M (mass of the thing moving) is very small, or that F is huge, and M is small.

For instance, the above sailboat can accelerate faster if it is lighter (lower M) and if the wind pushing it is stronger (bigger F).

Similarly, the jet ski will accelerate faster if the engine can generate more thrust, keeping the engine weight constant, or if the jet ski and rider are lighter for the same engine power.

All of this means that, with the known laws of physics, the extraordinary accelerations reported with UAPs suggest that someone, somewhere, has figured out how to generate either enormous F or very small M, or both big F and small M.

Imagine, for instance, that you see a normal-sized jet ski zipping across the water at 500 miles an hour, accelerating from a standstill to full speed in one second. It must be true that the jet ski's engine can produce prodigious force (F) relative to the mass (M) of the engine, the onboard fuel, the jet ski body, and the rider at a constant acceleration of roughly 22 G (9 G's is the upper limit of what humans can survive).

Here we have all the elements of the propulsion mystery with the force produced by a propulsion source and all the mass it must push or pull, including the propulsion source itself, the vehicle, the occupant, and the fuel that drives the propulsion system, all of which, collectively make up M.

Let's now dive into the UFO propulsion mystery by first reviewing non-mysterious methods of applying F to M to achieve A in the air.

Birds, bats, and flying insects fly by using the force of their wing muscles (F) to push air molecules in the opposite direction they wish to fly, transferring opposite momentum to the mass of their bodies (M) and making them accelerate (A) through the air. Here, a duck's wings push air molecules down and back to scoot it forward.

Credit: Hari K Patibanda Creative Commons Attribution 2.0 Wikimedia Commons

Or, if you're struggling with the duck thing, remember what it feels like to swim as your arms, acting as fins, push water in one direction so that you can move through the water in the other direction.

There's a little more to flying (or swimming, for that matter) than that, of course, involving Bernoulli's law, lifting airfoil shapes that push air at different velocities above and below the wings, and whatnot, but it all starts with good old F pushing on M to achieve A. (1)

The first aircraft moved through the air using propellers, basically powerful fans that suck in air in front and blow it out the back, producing rapid airflow over wings that are specially shaped to provide lift in precisely the way that your hand moves up in the Windstream of a car if you place it out the window. In contrast, the car moves at a decent clip.

If rotated up, propellers can push air down, allowing the craft to fly forward, move up and down, or hover, as shown below. Forgive us for oversimplifying here, as all propellers are moving airfoils that create their own "lift " from asymmetric airflow across their surfaces (which is why hovercraft propellers are also wings). But the main point remains: The atoms that make up a propeller aircraft move in one direction because air molecules are forced in the opposite direction.

Credit: Schoro29Creative Commons Attribution-Share Alike 4.0 Wikimedia Commons

This explains how control surfaces on airplanes cause aircraft to pitch, roll, and yaw: When a rudder in the rear of the craft pushes into the airstream, an asymmetric lateral torque is exerted by that airstream onto that surface, causing a yawing (left/right) rotation of the craft.

Now you're beginning to understand how baffling it is that UFOs without airfoils (wings) to provide lift, control surfaces to rotate (such as rudders, flaps, and ailerons), air intakes, air exhaust, propellers, or any other means of expelling mass can do what they do.

Jet engines can be considered a particular case of propellers, or a sequence of enclosed multiple propellers, that suck air in one end and blow it out the other end.

Jets generate more thrust than propellers because they compress and heat the air, significantly increasing its exit velocity from the rear of the engine and, thus, the forward velocity of the aircraft.

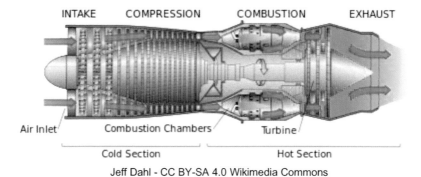

INTAKE COMPRESSION COMBUSTION EXHAUST

Air Inlet Combustion Chambers Turbine

Cold Section Hot Section

Jeff Dahl - CC BY-SA 4.0 Wikimedia Commons

Jet engines can also rotate to provide vertical thrust, like this hovering F-35.

Credit: US Marine Corps

Jets can fly much faster than propeller craft, but they still need wings for lift and control surfaces to maneuver. So, a lot of UFOs do not look like jets.

The ultimate "air-breathing" aircraft is a hypersonic vehicle, such as the Russian's new Kh-47M2 Kinzhal missile or NASA's X43A, shown below.

Credit: NASA

Like a jet, it sucks in, compresses, and superheats air molecules while pushing them out the back, but unlike a jet, it has no moving blades or propellers.

Instead, it uses a rocket to get it up to speed. The super high velocity initialized by the rocket allows air flowing into a specially shaped ramjet to super-heat and compress that air for truly astonishing velocities (Mach 9).

But even hypersonic craft still need airfoils and moving control surfaces to maneuver.

True rockets, however, do not require airfoils per se to stay aloft. Rockets are tubes filled with fuel and an engine to burn that fuel, often with maneuvering fins, but not wings for lift. Rockets ignite chemical fuel and push hot exhaust gas out of the back at a prodigious speed to move the rocket forward. Rocket engines can be dynamically angled to change the rocket's path, or fins on the rocket can change the rocket's pitch, roll, and yaw as desired. Note the maneuvering fins on this rocket.

Credit: David Monniaux CC BY-SA 4.0 Wikimedia Commons

Strictly speaking, rockets can maneuver without fins, using vectored thrust as they do in space, or as shown below with a rocket landing vertically, with lots of precise finless attitude control after a test launch.

Credit: NASA

But even lacking wings or control surfaces, vectored thrust rockets still need an engine, some observable moving parts (pivotable rocket thrusters) or some form of exhaust, and an aerodynamic shape that minimizes air resistance.

Which, mysteriously, quite a few UFOs, like the roughly one-third of all credible UFO reports that describe orbs or spheres, conspicuously lack.

Not that an onboard power source that generates heat, exhaust, or light is necessary.

Credit US Navy

Like the US Navy's weapon above, electromagnetic rail guns propel an inert ferromagnetic projectile at hefty velocities about 15,000 miles an hour. But even without any internal power, aerodynamics still requires a sleek rocket-like shape, and maneuvering requires movable control surfaces, which is why railgun projectiles look like those in the drawing below, not orbs or spheres, ovals, Tic Tacs or cigars.

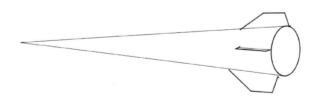

But the rail gun concept does raise a critical point: It's a lot easier for something to accelerate if it could shed all the mass (M) associated with an onboard engine and fuel and instead accelerate by being pulled or pushed by an external force. An outside force, remotely powered, removes all that inconvenient M from an onboard engine and fuel.

NASA has already taken the first step in this direction by eliminating the need for heavy rocket fuel, which must propel itself, and replacing it with very light-weight ionized gas.

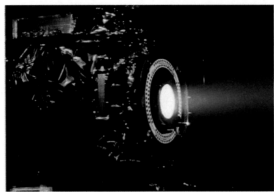
Credit: NASA

Such ionized gas drives(above) have no rocket fuel at all in the traditional sense but instead accelerate ionized gas out the back of the spacecraft, using strong electric or magnetic fields to grab charged molecules of gas (like argon) and push them out the rear, generating forward thrust by transfer of momentum. Changing the direction in which the ion beam nozzle points will change the vehicle's flight path. Ion drives can generate as much as ten times the amount of thrust per pound as chemical rocket engines. But ion thrust builds much more slowly than thrust from rocket fuel, so ion drives don't get spacecraft off the ground and into space. Instead, ion drives change the attitude of spacecraft once they leave the atmosphere. Ion engines also slowly but surely push the craft over long distances after chemical rockets have gotten them into the vacuum of space.

In its never-ending quest to eliminate *all* fuel–even lightweight ionized gas – NASA has developed spacecraft that have no engine or onboard fuel whatsoever but are propelled by the solar wind or powerful external lasers whose emitted photons strike large, ultrathin sheets called "light sails." Although massless, when photons strike light sails, they transfer forward momentum to those sails, just as air molecules in wind transfer momentum to nautical sails, propelling the craft forward.

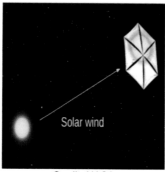

Solar wind

Credit: NASA

Yet another way to eliminate all onboard fuel and its associated inertia is to take the ion drive concept one step further. If a vehicle maneuvers in the atmosphere, it can use the surrounding air itself as an ion fuel source by distributing high voltage electrodes on the surface of the vehicle to ionize the surrounding air. Then, by applying strong magnetic or electrostatic fields, a craft can push those newly generated ions in directions that will propel the craft in the opposite direction. These drives are called Electroaerodynamic Drives (EAD) or silent, solid-state drives.

Here's an artist's rendering of MIT's proposed version of an EAD-propelled aircraft, where the wing surfaces have electrodes distributed on them that ionize and then propel atmospheric gases to generate thrust. (2)

Credit: NASA

NASA has also levitated engine-less, fuel-less flying saucers with powerful, invisible laser beams that propel the craft (next page) by forming heated plasmas generating shockwaves that push the craft along the laser's path.

Credit: NASA

Recall our earlier thought experiment with a jet ski that accelerates from zero to 500 MPH in one second. Suppose that the hypothetical jet ski lacked any obvious light sail (which would have to be positively enormous and driven by an equally prodigious ultra-high-power laser to overcome the inertia of the jet ski). In that case, it must have an awe-inspiring internal power source and ultra-efficient, lightweight, compact fuel for that power source to generate the required prodigious Force (F). (3)

No known chemical (e.g., gasoline or rocket fuel) energy source could move the jet ski so swiftly, which brings us to the question: If you can't harness chemical energy to get that much power in a small, light package, what *can* you do?

In exploring this question, we get to the heart of what must be going on if the UAPs are physical objects: they almost certainly use non-chemical energy sources and non-chemical-consuming power plants.

What packs the most punch in the slightest, lightest package?

Einstein answered with his famous equation, $E = MC^2$, which says that the amount of energy, E you can get by converting mass, M into energy is the multiple of that mass by the square of the speed of light, C (sorry, we lied about F=MA being the only equation, but that's the end of it, honest).

So, just one pound of mass on a vehicle, when converted to energy, would produce 40,766,849,157,300, 672 Joules of energy, roughly the same as a one Megaton nuclear explosion that could flatten all of Manhattan.

In the limit, the lightest, most efficient form of fuel and propulsion would be 100% efficient mass conversion to energy. The only way we know of to do that is to collide matter with antimatter to annihilate both matter and antimatter, releasing the energy bound up in both of their masses.

Although no one is seriously contemplating putting a matter-antimatter drive on a jet ski to drive it at 500 MPH, the NASA Innovative Advanced Concepts

(NIAC) program is investigating matter-anti-matter space drives, as shown on the next page, where matter (blue grid) and antimatter (red grid) are kept separate until it's time to combine them to generate energy and thrust. (2)

Matter-Antimatter

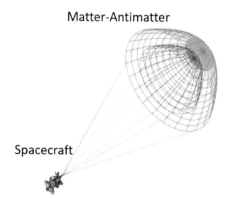

Spacecraft

Credit: NASA

Turning matter into energy has the advantage that the craft is lighter as mass is expended, helping to accelerate the craft even more for the same amount of thrust/force.

But even with this most efficient possible means of producing force, there remain thorny problems to solve in achieving humungous A with humungous F: There must be significant M (mass) to contain and separate matter from antimatter, such as electronics that produce electrons (like an old TV tube) and whopping magnetic coils to form the magnetic, non-contact containment field for positrons, because you can't contain antimatter in anything made of ordinary matter because the antimatter would combine with that ordinary matter to blow up the craft.

Additional M might be needed for what is called *propulsion mass*. Jets and rockets move forward by rapidly pushing out mass in the form of air or superheated gasses from rocket fuel combustion or ionized gas (such as hydrogen) out their back end (more about ion gas drives later).

Or, if you find rocket science intimidating, think of the jet ski moving forward by pushing water out its back end. As the water departs the jet ski engine in one direction, it gives a proverbial kick in the ass to the jet ski in the opposite direction.

If you're still having trouble wrapping your head around the idea of moving in one direction by exerting force in the opposite direction, think about how you jump off the ground: you move *up* against gravity by explosively pushing *down* on the ground with your legs.

So, one way to convert energy from matter annihilation into forward movement is to use that energy either to compress and heat some gas to spit out the back or to create whopping magnetic or electric fields to accelerate ionized gas (gas whose molecules have a positive or negative charge) out the back. If you want something to move in one direction, you need to spew something else in the opposite direction.

But that something else doesn't necessarily have to be mass. Thanks to Einstein's $E = MC^2$, we know that mass and energy are equivalent, and both have momentum, so you can push an object with mass forward by pushing photons out the back. For instance, combining electrons and positrons creates gamma rays, which, when directed out the back of a craft, will move the craft forward with the same momentum they leave it.

Even dispensing with conventional propulsion mass such as rocket fuel, however, does not necessarily reduce the total M of the craft because some M is required, such as gamma-ray reflecting mirrors (which could get quite heavy) to bounce the gamma rays off so that they go in the desired direction.

Gamma rays, by themselves aren't the most efficient propulsion "ejecta" because, as photons, they don't carry all that much momentum, so scientists who fantasize about antimatter drives use strong magnetic fields to focus and direct all manner of charged particles from other reactions such as controlled proton/antiproton collisions.

The point is that there is no free lunch when it comes to zipping around with the apparent accelerations that UAPs exhibit. Even with a hyper-efficient antimatter drive, the challenges of keeping M low to enable prodigious A's (e.g., by ultra-advanced material science) are formidable.

For those of you who are curious what other known forms of advanced propulsion, apart from antimatter drives, could produce such amazing accelerations, this chapter has an addendum summarizing NASA's Innovative Advanced Concepts (NIAC) program on propulsion, which is not only funding far-out ideas, such as antimatter drives, but other ideas such as fusion drives, laser drives and something called relativistic Mach effect drives.

If you aren't inclined to wade through the summaries of NASA's funded work on advanced propulsion, here are three takeaways relevant to UFOs.
1) In theory, astonishing accelerations can occur in many ways, according to the known laws of physics.
2) They all require hyper-advanced and efficient ways of producing energy and equally hyper-advanced material science to create lightweight substances that can contain and direct that energy.
3) Some advanced propulsion and aerodynamic systems on the drawing boards, such as silent bi-directional supersonic flight systems, would behave in the startling ways many UFOs behave, traveling at supersonic speeds with no sonic booms.

.
Why does all this rocket science matter for understanding how UFOs move and who moves them?

Let's apply what we've just learned about ultra-advanced propulsion science by starting with what it implies about discovering how UFOs can do what they do.

The main point here is that different possible propulsion systems, whether internal to the craft or external via directed energy, are, as far as we know from publicly available information, still at the small-scale laboratory demonstration stage or, like matter-antimatter drives, still in the realm of theoretical physics.

This leaves five possibilities for UAP propulsion.

1) Someone on Earth has secretly made a quantum leap in hyper-efficient propulsion and material science, even harnessing physics we don't know is possible (Chapter 3). This possibility is less far out than you might think, given that China and Russia both blew past the US in deploying hypersonic weapons.

2) Mother nature is the culprit, with ball lightning, rare meteorological effects, or effects we don't yet understand (Chapter 4).

3) Someone on Earth performs magic tricks to create the *illusion* of ultra-advanced propulsion. Remotely controlled laser plasmas could do this, but, as we'll see in Chapter 5, there are numerous other ways to trick the eye.

4) Someone not from this Earth has brought hyper-advanced propulsion here (Chapter 6).

5) There is a possibility that our limited human brains will never understand UFOs.

Before moving to the next chapter, exploring physics that we don't know is possible but don't yet believe is impossible, we'll dwell on possibility number 5: that we will never fully grasp the UFO phenomena.

If you're like us, you probably think that life has sprung up elsewhere in the vast universe and that, with the gazillions of habitable planets out there (300 million in our galaxy alone, by SETI's estimates, and there are billions of such galaxies in the universe) intelligent life has also evolved.

Given that the universe is over 13 billion years old, it's not outrageous to suppose that a few of those intelligent species are, say, a few hundred million years ahead of us in evolution, roughly the same span separating us from our very first vertebrate ancestors (about 500 million years ago, give or take).

Could those first vertebrates, although far more intelligent than their ancestors' single-cell organisms, ever get their fishy heads around an iPad? Sure, they could see the iPad, hear the sounds coming from it, feel its glassy smoothness, smell it, taste it, maybe even pick up electric fields emanating from it, but would they ever be capable of understanding its function, let alone the science and technology that made it work?

It would be the height of hubris to believe humans are the apex of evolution in the universe (although it could nevertheless be true), so it follows that it's entirely possible, if not likely, that some other species have come here or sent automated probes here, that we have no hope of understanding.

Such a scenario could answer one perplexing question: If ETs have indeed come here, either in "person" or through "unmanned" probes, why haven't they announced their presence on the one hand or gone to more extraordinary lengths to *hide* that presence on the other hand?

Well, if we sent astronauts or a probe to a planet whose life forms had barely evolved to the early vertebrate stage, would we announce our presence to those primitive creatures or take the trouble to hide our presence from them?

But it's still worth speculating how such advanced beings could cross interstellar space to get here, because these guesses might point the way to genuinely exotic possibilities for propulsion.

We shall now take up those possibilities as we consider physics that some physicists think is not impossible.

References

1) https://www.cam.ac.uk/research/news/how-wings-really-work

2)https://www.nasa.gov/niac-funded-studies

3)https://www.sciencedirect.com/science/article/abs/pii/S0030399217302062

Addendum

All but two concepts outlined here are for long distance traveling through the vacuum of outer space. Nevertheless, all NIAC concepts apply F to an M to achieve A in manners that could move objects in the atmosphere where observers have reported almost all UFOs. Therefore, it's instructive to study all the exotic propulsion systems which NASA has funded in NIAC.

More to the point for solving the UFO mystery, all these advanced concepts would produce some observable phenomena associated with propulsion, usually light or radiation, or sonic booms. These propulsion systems also dictate the shapes of the vehicles they power, shapes we can compare with UFO sightings to assess the likelihood that UFOs achieve remarkable performance using advanced engine designs on NASA's drawing board.

Pulsed Fusion Fission Drive

This rocket motor uses a nuclear fission reaction to generate intense X-rays that compress and heat a capsule containing hydrogen isotopes of deuterium and tritium, causing those isotopes to fuse into helium molecules, releasing prodigious amounts of energy that a nozzle directs out the back of the rocket, propelling the vehicle forward.

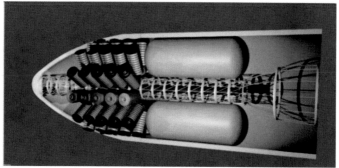

Credit NASA

Photonic laser thruster

Photon pressure is too weak to do more than slowly accelerate a spacecraft with a light sail. But that momentum can be amplified many times by bouncing laser photons back and forth between a mirror on the back of a mission vehicle and a corresponding mirror on a "resource vehicle" trailing the mission vehicle, as shown below. The same amplified photon pressure that pushes the mission vehicle forward also pushes the resource vehicle backward. But if the mass of the resource vehicle is much larger than that of the mission vehicle, it will move backwards much less than the lighter vehicle moves forward, so that the separation between the two vehicles will grow slowly.

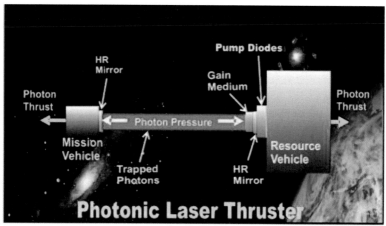

Credit: NASA

Photophoretic lift system

When solids heat up non-uniformly, with one side warmer than the other, air molecules on the warmer side will have more kinetic energy than corresponding molecules on the cooler side of the solid. The kinetic energy of the warmer molecules causes them to collide with the solid object with more force than air molecules on the cooler side, producing net pressure from the warmer side. When aircraft use engineered metamaterials that gather more heat on the lower side of the craft from solar illumination than on the upper half of the vehicle, uneven photophoretic pressure provides lift to the aircraft. Such aircraft have no engines, moving parts, or exhaust.

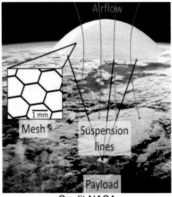

Credit NASA

Remote 100 MW laser propulsion using photovoltaics tuned to the laser wavelength

Remote high-power lasers can propel light-sail-equipped spacecraft with photon pressure, but they can also remotely deliver power and thrust by activating photovoltaic cells to provide power for high-voltage ion drive thrusters.

We show such a system below, where a 100-Megawatt laser array near Earth beams energy to a photovoltaic cell that is tuned to the wavelength of the laser to achieve 70% efficient conversion of laser power to electrical power for ion thrusters. The ion of choice in this application is Lithium, which is stored as lightweight solid fuel on the spacecraft. The laser energy not converted to power does exert extra thrust from photon pressure, but that extra thrust is small compared to that of the ion thruster.

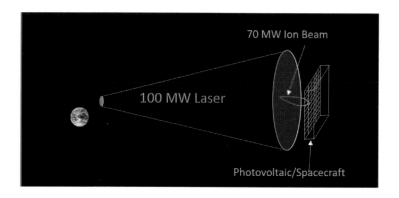

Pellet beam propulsion

Another way to use a remote laser to propel a spacecraft is to aim the laser at small pellets ejected out the back of the craft, heating the pellets to extreme temperatures that form plasmas on the laser side of the pellets, accelerating the pellets at over 100 KM/S into a plate on the back of the spacecraft, imparting forward momentum to the spacecraft.

Laser-heated pellet propulsion can push much heavier spacecraft than laser/light sail systems because the momentum transfer from pellet mass is much larger than that from massless photons.

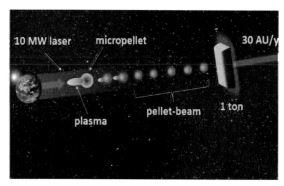

Credit: NASA

Ambient plasma wave propulsion

Many planets, such as Earth, have plasmas of ionized particles in their upper atmospheres that can serve as propellent when the spacecraft uses magnetic or electrostatic drives that suck in plasma at one end and expel it from the other.

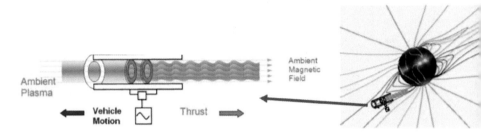

Credit: NASA

Nuclear electric propulsion

Small nuclear reactors aboard spacecraft can generate a lot of heat in a small space. Thermoelectric devices can then convert that heat into high voltage to accelerate ionized gas out of a nozzle, propelling the spacecraft. When mission vehicles require more mass than remote lasers can propel, a nuclear electric engine can be a good choice.

Credit: NASA

Brane spacecraft

Brane spacecraft use many distributed, efficient electrospray thrusters for propulsion.

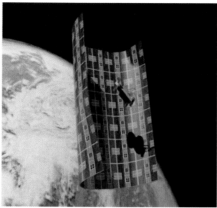
Credit NASA

Unlike traditional, rigid spacecraft, the brane is thin and flat, resembling a giant piece of wrapping paper.

Here's how it works:

The Brane Craft is about 30 microns thick, roughly half the width of a human hair. This extreme thinness gives it several advantages:

- Reduced Mass: It's incredibly lightweight, which translates to lower fuel consumption and higher maneuverability.
- Low Profile: Its minimal drag profile makes it aerodynamically efficient, leading to better fuel economy.
- Shape Shifting: The Brane Craft can morph its shape for various tasks, like deploying solar panels or capturing debris, due to its flexibility.
- The design incorporates an experimental ionic liquid thruster system. These electrosprays use ionic liquids, a new class of propellants, to generate thrust efficiently.
- These thrusters offer a high thrust-to-weight ratio, meaning they can produce significant thrust relative to the Brane Craft's weight.

Gradient Field Imploding Liner Fusion Propulsion System/Direct Conversion Fusion Drive

The imploding liner gradient field fusion drive works as follows:

- A hollow, superconducting electromagnet produces an ultra-strong magnetic field in its core.

- Nuclear fusion fuel, in the form of deuterium and tritium isotopes of Hydrogen is placed in liners (tubes) that implode under the intense magnetic fields.

- When fuel tubes shoot through the magnet's core the intense magnetic field compresses the tube, increasing pressure and temperature of the fuel to fuse Hydrogen isotopes into Helium, releasing prodigious amounts of radiation and heat.

- This superheated material continues out the back of the magnet into a nozzle that concentrates the flow into an extremely high exit velocity, propelling the spacecraft forward.

- The spacecraft accelerates every time a new tube of nuclear fuel shoots through the magnet.

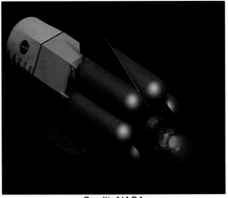

Credit: NASA

Diffractionless Beamed Propulsion

All the laser propulsion systems that we have described so far suffer from spreading out of the laser beam as it travels through space. This spreading decreases the energy density inside the laser beam, reducing the total amount of laser energy transferred to a spacecraft if the beam expands to a diameter larger than the light sail, photovoltaic cell or pellet.

Laser beam spreading results from optical diffraction (scattering). Loss of energy through beam spreading can be eliminated, however, if the laser travels in a waveguide, such as a fiber optic cable. The laser power system creates a laser waveguide in space, by confining the laser beam with neutral particles.

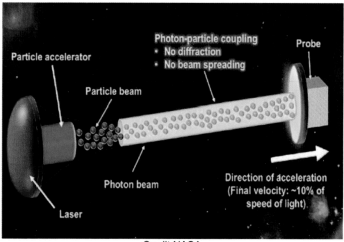

Credit NASA

Aneutronic Fusion Drive

In a conventional fusion drive, hydrogen nuclei (protons) fuse to form helium, releasing a large amount of energy and many neutrons and uncharged particles that can harm spacecraft materials and crew.

Conversely, aneutronic fusion involves fusion reactions that produce fewer or no neutrons. One example of an aneutronic fusion reaction is the fusion of helium-3 (He-3) and deuterium (D), which produces helium-4 (He-4) and a proton (H+). This reaction releases energy primarily from charged particles, efficiently converting into thrust.

A fusion chamber contains and facilitates the aneutronic fusion reaction within the spacecraft. The fuel, typically in the form of plasma, is heated to extremely high temperatures and pressures to initiate and sustain the fusion reactions.

The energy released during the aneutronic fusion reactions is in the form of high-speed charged particles (helium ions and protons). This energy can be efficiently converted into electricity using electromagnetic fields or other methods.

The electricity generated powers electric thrusters, such as ion thrusters or other advanced propulsion systems. These thrusters expel the charged particles at high velocities, creating thrust.

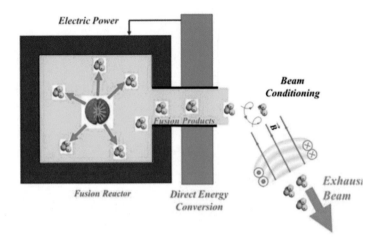

Credit: NASA

Radioisotope positron propulsion

Antimatter propulsion is a theoretical concept involving annihilating antimatter (e.g., positrons) with matter to release tremendous energy. The energy released from the annihilation can propel the spacecraft. Here's a simplified explanation of how an antimatter propulsion system might work:

Positrons, the antimatter counterparts of electrons, must be produced using specialized methods or particle accelerators.

Positrons are typically short-lived and must be stored in a containment system, such as a Penning trap, to prevent them from being annihilated with matter before they generate propulsion energy.

When the positrons escape containment, they encounter regular matter, such as hydrogen or another propellant. Upon contact with matter, positrons annihilate with electrons, releasing energy as gamma-ray photons.

Gamma-ray photons released during annihilation can be converted into electricity using gamma-ray detectors and photovoltaic cells.

The electricity generated from the annihilation process powers electric thrusters, such as ion thrusters or other advanced propulsion systems. These thrusters expel charged particles at high speeds to create thrust, propelling the spacecraft.

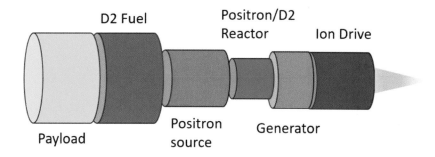

Fission fragment rocket engine

The core of a fission fragment rocket contains fissile material such as uranium-235 (U-235) or another suitable isotope. Under the right conditions, the fissile materials can undergo nuclear fission, where the nucleus of an atom splits into two smaller nuclei, releasing a large amount of energy.

In addition to releasing energy, nuclear fission produces high-speed fragments as a byproduct. These fragments are typically heavy, charged particles, such as ions, expelled in opposite directions with extremely high velocities.

The high-speed fragments flow into a magnetic nozzle. This nozzle is a crucial component of the fission fragment rocket. It uses magnetic fields to channel and focus the fragments in one direction, creating a high-velocity exhaust jet.

The directed fragments, moving at a significant fraction of the speed of light, provide an extremely high exhaust velocity. This high velocity is essential for efficient spacecraft propulsion, as it follows the basic principles of rocketry, where a high exhaust velocity generates greater thrust for a given amount of fuel.

As the high-speed fragments exit the nozzle, they generate thrust according to Newton's third law of motion, where for every action, there is an equal and opposite reaction. The expulsion of the fragments at high velocities produces forward thrust, propelling the spacecraft in the opposite direction.

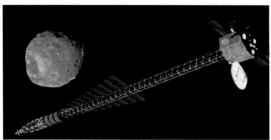
Credit: NASA

Bi-directional silent supersonic flying wing

The supersonic bi-directional flying wing uses a unique aerodynamic design to maintain stability and control in forward and reverse flight. The aircraft's wings and body shape minimize drag and maintain maneuverability in both directions.

The aircraft might feature variable geometry wings or other components to optimize performance in different flight modes. For example, the wings might change their sweep angle or shape to adapt to supersonic forward flight, subsonic forward flight, or reverse flight.

The aircraft requires a propulsion system capable of generating thrust in both directions.

The aircraft may use thrust vectoring technology, which involves altering the direction of the engine's exhaust to control the aircraft's pitch and yaw. The aircraft can achieve reverse flight by redirecting thrust in the opposite direction.

Advanced flight control systems are necessary to manage the transition between forward and reverse flight modes and ensure stability and safety during these maneuvers. These systems must adjust the aircraft's control surfaces, engine thrust, and other parameters accordingly.

Supersonic flight generates significant heat due to air compression and friction. The aircraft needs advanced materials and heat management systems to withstand the high temperatures associated with supersonic flight.

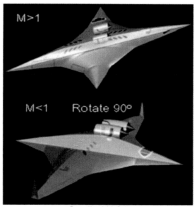

Credit: NASA

What these advanced NASA concepts imply about UFO

At the end of the next chapter, we'll assess in greater detail whether these NASA propulsion systems, or even more advanced concepts that aren't impossible in theory, might explain the incredible performance and unusual appearance of UFOs.

But before we dive into the exotic realm of "might be possible", it's worth briefly taking stock of where we stand explaining UFO behavior with advanced but known technologies we've just discussed.
 We do this because many (if not most) physicists believe the far-out concepts in the next chapter, which include faster than light space drives and time travel, aren't possible. Which means that, together with existing propeller, jet, rocket, ion and remote laser power drive systems, NASA's advanced concepts, or ones very like them, are our best bet for explaining how someone could make UFOs fly the way they do.

And not just fly the way they do but look the way they do and sound the way they do (or don't when they're silent).

Comparing UFO behavior and appearance to craft that use advanced propulsion isn't straightforward because UFOs come in many flavors. According to the Pentagon's AARO, around 30% of credible unexplained sightings are moving or hovering lights, while a similar percentage are solid orbs or spheres. Some UFOs are rectangular, others triangular, oval or Tic Tac shaped. And none of the credible UFOs had moving control surfaces, exhaust or moving parts of any kind, nor have any UFOs yet been observed radiating heat.

We do not need to posit exotic NASA NIAC designs as explanations for UFOs that hover, move with flight patterns like those of craft with propeller, jet, hypersonic or rocket engines, because, in theory, these conventional propulsion systems could cause aircraft to move in the relatively "normal" ways some UFO's move. Even if observers did not get close enough or look long enough to spot telltale signs of conventional power plants, control surfaces or thrust vectoring, those ordinary features could have been obvious under the right viewing conditions. For instance, high performance drones carrying bright lights, or rockets flying at night would look like some of the hovering, streaking lights that have been reported.

Multiple external lasers, which push on a craft from different angles wouldn't require moving surfaces on the craft, but they would require the craft to have large cross sections to collect laser energy efficiently (unlike those of UFOs). And laser photon pressure is too weak to produce the instantaneous accelerations that have been reported.

Shockwaves from focused laser plasmas might push lightweight craft more briskly, but they emit bright light, very unlike many UFOs, such as those reported by Naval aviators. And no existing laser drive system, even on the drawing boards, could cause radical turns, stops, long loiter periods, and accelerations of UFOs.

Thus, when UFOs accelerate, stop, climb, and turn like no known aircraft or laser propulsion system, we do need to look closely at the most advanced propulsion systems on the drawing board for possible explanations (at least human-origin explanations).

In doing this, we can simplify the comparison of exotic propulsion systems to UFO behavior and appearance by narrowing our focus to the most extreme cases, such as the 2004 Navy reports and similar Navy reports from operations over the Atlantic in 2015. That way, we can ask the thought-provoking question: can even the most advanced propulsion system on the drawing board explain the extraordinary behavior and appearance of fastest-flying, fastest-maneuvering UFOs? The short answer is no.

First, except for the photophoretic, ambient plasma and bi-directional supersonic craft, all the NASA NIAC designs are for travel in the vacuum of space, not Earth's atmosphere. Thus, these designs focus on high-end speed (and fuel economy) in one direction, not ultra-fast turns and jarring stops. Also, these spaceships don't look like orbs, triangles, Tic Tacs and other reported shapes.

Except for the Brane vehicle that employs liquid ion thrusters, all propulsion systems we have considered, including photophoretic craft, emit either light, heat, or exhaust plumes, and all would make a lot of noise in fast flight. And the membranous Brane doesn't resemble any UFO.

The bidirectional "silent" supersonic aircraft would not generate sonic booms, but it operates with a lot of heat and has visible engines and exhaust. The bidirectional craft couldn't turn and stop the way some UFOs do, either.

OK, so if both conventional and exotic designs on the drawing boards can't explain the highest performing UFOs, can even more exotic designs that might exist in the realm of highly speculative physics hold the answers?

The next chapter will tell us.

References

1) https://www.nasa.gov/niac-funded-studies/

3.   Exotic propulsion that's not impossible

Claiming something isn't impossible is not to assert that it's possible. Rather, such claims only mean our understanding of the universe has not ruled out some possibilities.

It's important to point out that only *some* reputable scientists believe these ideas aren't impossible.

Many reputable scientists believe all ideas described in this chapter, such as wormhole travel or warp drives, *are i*mpossible.

And, from what we now know of physics, the probability that these strange and beautiful concepts for zipping through space are viable is exceedingly low.

So, why waste time describing ideas that are extremely unlikely to work, let alone explain the behavior of UFOs?

Well, the reason goes back to what we said earlier about historical quantum leaps in our understanding of nature (such as continental drift): Before the fact, all of these ideas were given zero to very low probability of being valid.

This means that, among the zillions of whacky theories for revolutionary propulsion, if history is a guide, one or two of those wild ideas will turn out, against all odds, to work.

In the spirit of that belief, we'll now dive into some truly unique ideas for traversing space.

But, given that space and time are on a four-dimensional continuum (spacetime), we will also look at how it might not be impossible to propel things forward or backward in time, and some of those things might be, you guessed it, UFOs.

The time dimension is a fascinating one to consider in examining UFOs because it carries a genuinely far-out possibility that UFOs have an Earthly origin, except that those Earthly beings –or their probes-are from the far distant past or sometime in the future. To say that UFOs have an Earthly origin does not automatically imply that *humans* are doing it, but instead raises the possibility (or rather non-impossibility) that *non*humans from Earth's far distant past or distant future are responsible for what we're seeing.

Yes, you're now getting a flavor of just how wild this chapter will be because, when you get right down to it, with some of the propulsion ideas we'll examine, such as wormhole travel, the difference between traveling through space and traveling through time gets, to say the least, *very* blurry.

Put another way, it might be just as easy to travel through time as it would be to traverse unimaginably vast distances of space in a short time, so one kind of exotic travel through space might not be more or less likely than moving through time.

So, buckle up as we take you on a wild ride through space and time.

Not impossible ways of traversing space

As with the flip phones that first appeared on Star Trek in the 1960s and made their way into users' hands less than 30 years later, science fiction sometimes gets it right to predict future breakthroughs.

Star Trek also featured ideas –such as matter transporters that beam people across space–that are unlikely ever to be possible, but other concepts from that show, such as warp drives and wormholes, are not currently considered –at least by some physicists-to be impossible.

For those who believe there's no point exploring such far-out ideas, it's worth pausing here to consider just how little we know about what's impossible.

Currently, we have no clue how to resolve science's biggest paradox: Einstein's General Relativity (the theory of gravity) has proven correct after innumerable attempts to disprove it, and quantum mechanics has similarly withstood all attempts to prove it wrong, so, as far as we know, both General Relativity and quantum mechanics are true, but they are incompatible with each other. General Relativity, for example, describes a smooth, deterministic, continuous fabric of spacetime, whereas the quantum world is probabilistic (not deterministic) and discretely fragmented.

Here's a visual way of thinking of science's biggest unresolved contradiction.

The upper line represents continuous spacetime in General Relativity, where no matter how much you magnify it, will always appear to be a continuous line.

But in the quantum world, where things come in discrete chunks, or quanta, that same line, under extreme magnification, would be discontinuous, like a dotted line in the middle, with nothing in between.

We say "sort of" because in quantum mechanics, you can't ever know the exact position and velocity of anything (Heisenberg uncertainty principle), and what we show as dots making up the line are clouds of dots representing the probability that any given dot is in any given place. So, if we were strictly rigorous, we would show each dot as a wave function, where each dot simultaneously occupied multiple places in and around the dot (fuzzy dots on their line). Thus, in our quantum dotted line, the position of each dot is just the highest probability location of that dot, when all the dots occupy multiple locations along the line. (1)

The bottom line is that we have no idea how the wildly different views of reality that General Relativity and quantum mechanics could be accurate, but they are both true.

This is another way of saying our understanding of what must be true or untrue is limited.

We are equally baffled about what makes up about 95% of the universe. Ordinary matter and energy that form the basis of current physics comprise only 5% of the universe (as far as we know). The other 95% consists of dark energy and dark matter: For both, we know much more about what they aren't than what they *are*.

Who knows, maybe the mysteries of quantum physics, dark energy, other weird forms of energy, and not-impossible propulsion are part of the same mystery. Later in this chapter, when we discuss wormholes and warp drives, a critical enabling concept, negative energy, does indeed grow out of quantum theory.

A way, way, way oversimplified explanation of spacetime to explain weird propulsion

When we talk about propulsion, we are talking about moving something from point A to point B at a specific rate; in other words, pushing or pulling something a certain distance in space over a particular time interval.

Thus, the only way to grasp weird concepts such as wormholes and warp drives is to understand at least a little about the underlying concepts of space and time.

We start with the strange fact that space and time aren't separate entities but closely intertwined in something called spacetime.

It's almost impossible for normal humans to visualize four dimensions, so here's one way of thinking about it.

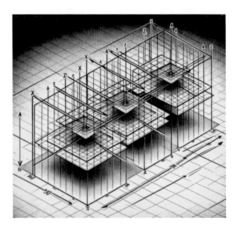

Above we see three identical three-dimensional coordinate systems at three distinct points in time from left to right, where the horizontal arrows going from left to right at the bottom of the graph represent the flow of time from past to present to future. You, for instance, occupy the center "now" coordinate system right now, but by the time you finish reading this sentence, you will occupy the one on the far right.

You have not changed (more or less), nor has your position in 3D space, but you have moved in time, so you have moved in spacetime.

If actual spacetime were neatly arrayed in nearly straight lines, as shown above, none of the truly exotic, currently non-impossible propulsion ideas would work. However, thanks to Einstein, we know that spacetime is not straight and flat but curved.

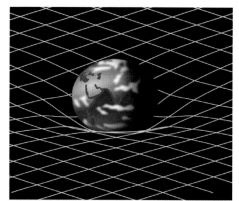

Credit: Mysid CCA-Share Alike 3.0 Wikimedia Commons

Think of spacetime as a rubber sheet that gets deformed by masses such as the Earth, like the proverbial bowling ball placed on the rubber sheet. Another term for this deformation is…. gravity. Objects moving in spacetime near the Earth will fall into its dimple and either roll "down" into Earth, curve past it (if going fast enough), or, like a marble thrown into a bowl, and running around the rim, circle the space around the Earth, precisely as the Moon circles the Earth, and as Earth circles the sun. What we think of as the attractive force of gravity is not a force, per se, like magnetic attraction, but an underlying property of spacetime itself.

Imagining an object zipping towards Earth and crashing into it, curving past it, or orbiting it, it is accurate to say that spacetime (warped by a planet's presence) dictates how objects with mass will move around in it. And conversely, mass dictates the shape of spacetime, a two-way relationship if you will.

Because mass and energy are different forms of the same thing (remember $E = MC^2$), electromagnetic energy also warps spacetime so that a photon zipping through space forms a (very) small dimple in spacetime as it moves.

If spacetime dictates how objects will move, it follows that one way to propel things at a speedy rate is to create an extreme spacetime distortion.

For instance, you could accelerate something to very near the speed of light (from your perspective) if you tossed it into a black hole, one of the most radical spacetime distortions. By analogy, a marble tossed down an incredibly steep slope will accelerate quickly!

This brings us to extreme distortions of spacetime, such as black holes, which astronomers have observed in nature, and wormholes, which might exist in theory, but no one has observed.

Travel via Black holes and Wormholes

When we say the ideas we're about to present are still possible, we mean that some, but far from all reputable physicists, think that General Relativity (that explains gravity) doesn't necessarily rule out these wild ideas. But that's a long way from saying that the concepts are possible. There isn't yet consensus on whether using extreme distortions of spacetime to zip from point A to point B at a significant fraction– or even multiple of the speed of light– is possible.

With that in mind, let's start with the non-impossibility of achieving ultra-fast travel using black holes.

An intuitive way to understand how to –theoretically–use black holes for accelerating to jaw-dropping speeds is to imagine that you are skiing down a nearly vertical slope.
Straight down the slope takes you directly into the "gravity well" of Earth's gravity.

The diagram below shows a "normal" gravity well on the left, with a sun forming a depression in spacetime. If you head directly downslope into the center of the well, you'll get going faster than you can control and experience a very bad day at the "bottom."

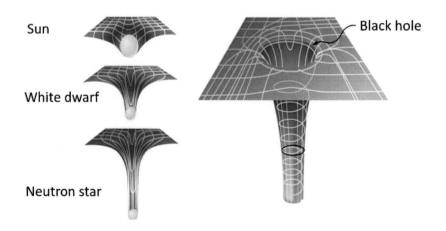

OpenStax University PhysicsCrdiet" CCA-Share Alike 3.0 Wikimedia Commons

But, as with a traverse on a ski slope, if you cut across the gravity well at an angle, you gain significant acceleration from the "well" without being sucked into it.

In space travel, such a traverse is called a gravitational slingshot maneuver. Probes sent to Mars, for example, head first for the Moon, at an angle, to gain some acceleration from the Moon's gravity before heading out to Mars. But the trajectories are calculated so that the craft does not get irreversibly sucked into the Moon's gravity well and experience what scientists call rapid deceleration and lay people call a fatal crash.

As the mass of a celestial object increases, so does the steepness of its gravity well, as shown above for a mundane planet, dense neutron star, and black hole, respectively.

Suppose the steepest gravity well is that of a black hole. In that case, it follows that the fastest acceleration from a gravitational slingshot maneuver would be to approach a black hole at an angle, carefully skirting the event horizon that marks the point of no return from the staggering pull of the black hole. In other words, close enough to accelerate towards where you want to go, but not so close that you get sucked into a direction that you do not want to go. Calculations show that, if successful, a black hole slingshot maneuver could get you up to a healthy fraction of the speed of light if you could manage some nasty side effects of getting close to the gravitational monster.

One of those nasty effects is extreme tidal force. Near a black hole, the gravitational force changes so rapidly over small distances that the part of your body closest to the blackhole feels much more of a tug than the part furthest from the hole, creating significant stress inside your body (and spacecraft), so that even if you skimmed the black hole's event horizon, you, and your craft could tear apart. Then there's the problem of extreme radiation in and around the black hole, to name just one of the many complications of black hole slingshotting.

There might be ways of counteracting such nastiness, which would make an extreme slingshot possible, but scientists don't yet know what effective countermeasures are.

Then there is also the inconvenient fact that if there are no black holes between you and where you wish to go, you can't accelerate to the desired velocity in the desired direction.

But things get even more weird and dangerous when contemplating travel through wormholes.

Shown below, a wormhole is a hypothesized tunnel through spacetime, possibly formed in association with a black hole or perhaps left over as an artifact from the early universe.

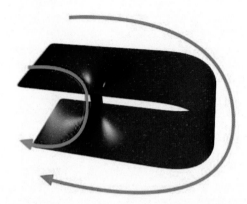

Credit: Panzi CCA-Share Alike 3.0 Wikimedia Commons

The red arrow shows a conventional path between two distinct parts of spacetime, while the green arrow shows a much shorter, faster path through a wormhole.

A wormhole represents such an extreme distortion of spacetime that one part of space connects with a far, far, far different region of space via extreme dimpling of spacetime in separate places towards each other.

If somehow, and that's a big somehow, one could traverse the "throat" of the wormhole without being crushed or torn apart, in theory, it would be not impossible to take a big shortcut through space, achieving what amounts to faster than light travel.

Credit: Digital art by Les Bossinas (Cortez III Service Corp.)1998 NASA

One idea about how to travel through the throat safely is through something called "negative energy," which, if judicially deployed in the throat, could keep it from collapsing and obliterating everything in it.

Neither wormholes nor negative energy have been proven to exist, but neither have they been disproven.

Oh, and as with black holes, if there are not any wormholes along the way to where you want to go, you can't, as they say, "get there from here."

How to create your own spacetime distortions to go fast

A few far-reaching thinkers who are unconvinced travel beyond light speed is impossible dare to hypothesize that, theoretically, it might not be impossible to get around Einstein's prohibition about traveling faster than light if the thing moving is not an object (such as a spacecraft) but spacetime itself.

A way, way, way oversimplified way to think of what we're about to describe—yes, you guessed it, warp drives—is to think of a surfer advancing towards the beach on a wave.

Credit: Shalom Jacobovitz CCA-Share Alike 3.0 Wikimedia Commons

As long as the wave does not break as it moves, the surfer can remain stationary with respect to the wave and let the wave do all the moving. Yes, surfers cut across moving waves, but that part isn't important right now.

The important part is that if one could create a traveling ripple in spacetime without moving at all inside that ripple (thereby keeping well below the speed of light inside your piece of spacetime), one could move as fast as the ripple moves.

And just how fast can spacetime itself move?

In defining a period of hyper-inflation of the universe immediately after the Big Bang, Dr. Alan Guth showed that it was likely that spacetime itself expanded far faster than the speed of light. Einstein's theories prohibit faster-than-light travel within spacetime; nothing in those theories prevents faster-than-light movement of spacetime itself.

Thus, with its visionary NIAC program, NASA has funded theoretical exploration of such a drive, the basic idea of which we show below.

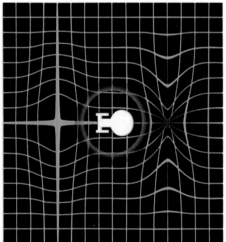

Credit: D Ipin Creative Commons Zero, Wikimedia Commons

A craft moving from left to right would use something called negative energy (distinct from dark energy) to expand spacetime behind the craft. Negative energy, which a few physicists hypothesize might exist, acts on spacetime the opposite way "positive" energy and mass do by *expanding,* not contracting spacetime. Simultaneously, in front of the craft, a whole lot of positive energy would create a compression of spacetime, so that the net effect would be the craft would be pushed by expanding spacetime behind them and pulled by a steep gravity well in front of them: Kind of like skiing straight down a slope with a very brisk tailwind pushing you from behind.

Although NASA has funded theoretical research on warp drives, along with other far-out ideas, the prestige of NASA doesn't necessarily lend credence to the existence of negative energy or even the theoretical viability of faster-than-light travel via warp drives. Such investments only mean that NASA, like your authors here, is keeping an open mind.

Other weirdities emerging from Relativity

Some theorists, such as James Woodward of the Space Studies Institute, believe that propellant-less propulsion might be possible by manipulating the distribution of rest mass in a spacecraft, locally changing inertia in an asymmetric manner that generates net motion in one direction. Woodward claims that by producing small, asymmetric changes in the mass distribution of piezoelectric wafers that expand and contract with applied voltage, small, but finite changes in inertia could cause the craft to move in one direction without fuel or ejection mass. The proposed mechanism of action is the Mach Effect, where complex interactions between the asymmetric inertia in the piezoelectric crystals with the gravitational field of the surrounding universe, create a net gravitational pull in one direction (8).

Although the net force would be minimal, with no air friction to oppose it over time, it could accelerate a craft, shown below, to very high speeds in outer space.

And it would have no visible exhaust, emitted light, radiation, or any other observable, although how it might maneuver is not established.

Many physicists aren't convinced that it's possible to move in one direction without being pushed by an external force or expelling mass or energy in the opposite direction of travel.

Credit: NASA

Another space drive that its inventors claim can achieve thrust without an external force or ejection of mass or energy is the Electromagnetic (EM) Drive. A few maverick scientists claim that the EM drive, shown below, generates net thrust through complex interactions of microwaves radiated by the drive into a resonating chamber. Research continues EM drives even though most physicists believe it can't work.

Credit NASA

Now, let's talk about time travel

Earlier in the chapter, we said that when you travel close to the speed of light, the prospect of traveling through time arises.

Such time travel is not science fiction but science fact due to what Einstein called time dilation.

If you were to synchronize two atomic clocks in Los Angeles and then take one of those clocks with you on a flight to New York, when you compared elapsed time on the two clocks after you landed in New York, you'd find that the clock that sat on the seat next to you (unless you put it in your lap) had advanced more slowly than the one that remained in California, due to time dilation.

Time dilation, which scientists have measured and replicated many times, is often explained by depicting a light clock that bounces photons (say from a laser) between two facing mirrors so that every bounce of a photon off a mirror represents a "tick" of the clock.

On the left, the clock is stationary, so the photons bounce back and forth in repeating up-down paths whose lengths never change. But when the two mirrors move together (sitting next to you on your cross-country flight), the clock's motion causes the paths to increase, as shown on the right below, because the photons are now heading towards moving, not stationary mirrors. The speed of light never changes, so the longer paths necessarily take longer for the light to bounce back and forth, meaning that the clock's ticks will be spaced further apart in time: ergo, time dilation.

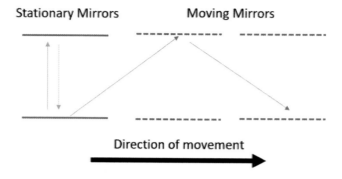

If this diagram hurts your head, here's a more straightforward way of thinking about time dilation that's not strictly speaking accurate but true enough to get the point across.

In a metaphorical sense, if time were a river that flowed at a certain speed, that speed would be.... the speed of light.

Therefore, just sitting there reading this, you are zipping through time at the speed of light.

As shown in the highly oversimplified diagram below, in which spacetime collapses to two dimensions, space and time, you can see that if you don't move at all in space, you move through time at the speed of light (red arrow). So, time passes completely "normally."

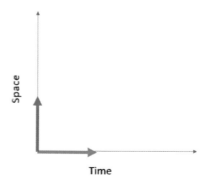

But the moment you start to move at some velocity through space because you're constantly moving at the same speed of light through spacetime, you have bled off some of your velocity through time. And, if you somehow manage to move through space at the speed of light (green arrow), you will completely stop moving through time, at least from the point of view of an external observer.

What does this have to do with UFOs?

Suppose (and we admit it's a very, very, *very* big suppose) that many millions of years ago, an intelligent species evolved that was capable of space travel. If that species learned how to harness some of the ideas earlier in this chapter to travel near the speed of light, they could travel out of the solar system and back to Earth, having aged, with respect to an observer on Earth, extraordinarily little.

Doing some math, if this hypothetical prehistoric species left Earth and traveled for 30 years out to space and back at .99999999999999 the speed of light, on Earth, 212 million years would have passed when they returned, even though our ancient space travelers would have only aged 30 years. A couple hundred million years of geological activity, including churning of the Earth's crust, erosion, continental drift and mountain formation might have masked the existence of earlier civilizations from paleontologists.

Therefore, although unlikely, it is theoretically possible that the UFOs are not ETs, nor advanced humans in our time, but from ancient Earthlings who have come home to check things out.

Now you see what we mean when we say that, in the limit, exotic travel through space and travel through time are not all that different.

At least, according to proven physics.

But would the unproven physics we've discussed in this chapter (e.g., wormholes and warp drives) allow Earthly visitors (and presumably UFOs) from our *future* to race around our skies today?

The overwhelming majority of reputable physicists today would emphatically say *no*: Tme only moves in one direction, forward, and that's that.

And yet, the cosmos harbors some weirdities that make you wonder.

For instance, rotating Kerr black holes have been observed that exhibit what's called "frame dragging," in which an area of spacetime outside the blockhole's so-called ergosphere gets "dragged" around with the spin of the black hole, potentially at a rotational velocity greater than the speed of light (remember, although nothing can move faster than light within spacetime, spacetime itself can move faster than the speed of light) creating what astrophysicists call a Closed Timelike Curve (CTC). (9)

The first image, below, is an artist's rendering of a rapidly spinning black hole, churning, and turning spacetime near it.

If spacetime were to accelerate around the black hole enough, then a CTC would be formed, as shown in an artist's concept below, in which someone traveling in the vicinity of the black hole (avoiding the event horizon so as not to be sucked in) would travel in a closed curve in spacetime, returning to the same point in space AND IN TIME, from which they departed.

Yes, indeed, such a journey constitutes backward travel in time.

CTCs, like wormholes and black holes, are valid mathematical solutions to Einstein's field equations of General Relativity. In theory, although it's admittedly a vast stretch, there might be a way for someone from the future to travel, or cause a probe to travel, back in time where it eventually pops into our sky as a UFO.

As with wormholes, because Einstein's field equations say CTCs are not impossible, there's zero proof that they exist.

Before we leave the subject of time travel...

Just as flying from LA to New York would slow an atomic clock relative to a stationary one, flying from orbit down to the Earth's surface would also slow such a clock down, and not just from the velocity of motion from orbit to Earth's surface, but from the stronger gravitational field experienced at Earth's surface.

Gravitational time dilation is slightly more complicated to explain without the math of metric tensors and other esoteric elements of Einstein's field equations. Still, we'll look at it with a crude, oversimplified analogy.

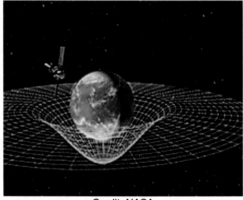

Credit: NASA

Above, we show the curvature of spacetime near the Earth, where a satellite is circling the rim of a bowl of spacetime.

But, relative to nearly flat spacetime far from Earth, closer to the Earth, time and space are also curved, and the amount of that curvature increases the closer you get to Earth. Hence, to an observer traveling in an un-curved part of space, someone traveling near the Earth's surface at the same velocity would take longer to get from point A to point B because the near-Earth traveler was traveling along a longer, curved path vs. the straight path taken by the distant observer.

Knowing this, we'll resurrect our ancient earthlings from the past and now posit that they traveled to a black hole (a stationary one this time with no frame-dragging), orbited just outside the event horizon at a healthy fraction of the speed of light for say, 30 years, then escaped orbit (not a mean feat, admittedly, but not impossible). Traveling in extreme curves through time just outside the black hole versus straight lines in flat spacetime, observers on Earth would see time pass for the ancient earthlings even slower than if they were traveling at the same speed through flat spacetime.

,
All of this means that if someone really wanted to see the distant future, they would fly fast and to a black hole with an enormous gravitational field that would dilate time even more. Calculations show that about a 3X increase in extra time dilation would be possible by orbiting a decent-sized black hole near the event horizon, slow enough to escape but fast enough to make time, from the point of view of an Earthly observer, really zip by.

What exotic propulsion possibilities –and non-impossibilities-mean for UFOs

We'll take stock of what we've learned in the last two chapters on exotic propulsion.

Here are pictures of different UFOs reported to the Pentagon, categorized as unresolved, meaning no satisfactory explanations have yet surfaced. In all of these cases, videos or radar data, or both, were collected, characterizing the range and velocity of movement along with changes in altitude. (2,3,4,5,6,7)

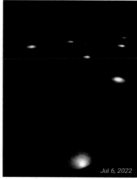

Jul 6, 2022

Credit US NAVY

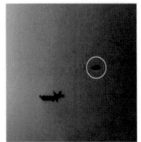

Credit: US NAVY

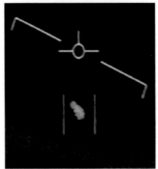

Credit US NAVY

Credit: US DOD AARO

Credit US Navy

The graphics below from the Pentagon's All Domain Anomaly Resolution Office (AARO) represent the wide range of phenomena that we are trying to understand, underscoring the diverse shapes, sizes, appearances, ways the UFOs have of moving around, and different altitudes at which they appeared. The range of appearances we must explain gets even more complicated when you consider that several reports, for which there are not yet satisfactory explanations, feature combinations of attributes such as triangle shapes that emit light. And, of course, when you get closer, something that is only a light in the distance could be a light carried by something else. (2)

REPORTED UAP-MORPHOLOGY

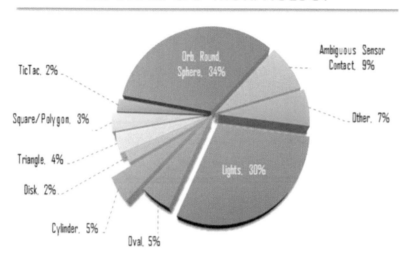

TicTac, 2%

Square/Polygon, 3%

Triangle, 4%

Disk, 2%

Cylinder, 5%

Oval, 5%

Orb, Round, Sphere, 34%

Lights, 30%

Ambiguous Sensor Contact, 9%

Other, 7%

Credit: US DOD AARO

TYPICALLY-REPORTED UAP CHARACTERISTICS

Appearance	Morphology	Round
	Size	1-4 Meters
	Color	White, Silver, Translucent
Performance	Altitude	10k – 30k feet
	Velocity	Stationary to Mach 2
	Propulsion	No thermal exhaust detected
Signatures	Radar	Intermittent, X-Band (8-12 GHz)
	Radio	1-3 GHz, 8-12 GHz
	Thermal	Intermittent, Shortwave Infrared, Medium-Wave Infrared

Credit: US DOD AARO

REPORTED-UAP ALTITUDES

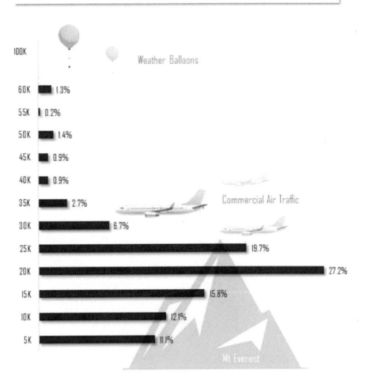

Credit: US DOD AARO

As a result, in applying our understanding of the art of the possible—or not impossible—propulsion, to the extent that UFOs aren't optical illusions or natural phenomena (next chapter), we have much explaining to do.

For instance, we must not only consider how different propulsion systems would influence the shape of a UFO but also whether a propulsion system in question would emit light, heat, or radiation or enable the rapid decelerations and abrupt changes in direction that some UFOs exhibit. And whether a particular propulsion system would emit any exhaust plume or have moving parts, such as rotating or pivoting a drive engine to change the direction of travel. For instance, ion drives would have to pivot around on the craft to cause a craft to decelerate or turn on a dime, and this movement should be evident.

Then, there's the genuine possibility that, for any individual UFO, there might be multiple propulsion systems, say one type to take the UFO long distances and another to maneuver locally. We do this now with chemical rockets that get spacecraft out of the atmosphere and ion drives that rotate and propel the craft into outer space.

To complicate matters further, we are still determining what some more exotic theoretical propulsion systems (think warp drives) would look like or what effects (emitted light, air turbulence, etc.) they would create.

For instance, in the atmosphere, a warp drive would strongly bend light rays near it, creating extraordinary optical effects, unlike those reported with UFOs.

Here is an artist's concept of what a massive distortion of spacetime of the type necessary for a warp drive, might look like. None of the UAP reports describe such a thing.

Having surfaced different types of propulsion either on the drawing boards, operational or hypothesized to be viable, we are now at a point where we can ask: Could any of these propulsion systems account for the virtuoso acrobatics associated with UFOs?

Taking up this question, as we did at the end of the preceding addendum, we will ignore UFO reports where the flight patterns were within performance envelopes of known propulsion and flight systems, and focus exclusively on cases, such as the Navy Tic Tac that no currently operational technology could achieve. We narrow the discussion to such boundary cases with the belief that, if we can attribute the extreme outliers to advanced propulsion systems, then we can surely explain the less sensational cases with known technology.

On the other hand, if the most advanced propulsion systems we know of, even in *theory*, can't explain the UFO flight patterns, we've got a real head-scratcher on our hands, decreasing the likelihood that the extreme UFOs arise from human technology.

	Vanish/appear	Zoom Fast	Turn Quick	Hover long time	Brake Fast	Climb Far Fast	No intake	No exhaust	No moving parts	No light sail	No light or heat	No sonic boom	No distorted air	No Aero shape
Prop Jet Rocket			?											
Hyper-sonic		?	?			?								
Rail Gun		X				X	X	X		X	X		X	
Photon press.		?		X		?	X	X	X	?	?		X	X
Nuclear		X	X	X	X	X	X			X				
Anti-matter		X	X	X	X	X	X	X	X	X				X
Warp	X	X	X	X	X	X	X	X	X	X	X	X		X
Mach effect							X	X	X	X	X			X
Plasma Display	X	X	X	X	X	X	X	X	X	X		X	X	X
Ion Drive							X	X	X	X				
Bi-directional												X		
Brane E-spray							X		X	X	X		X	X

That said, let us start the analysis.

Among the most inexplicable UFOs are the 2004 Navy sightings of non-aer-odynamically shaped objects, with no control surfaces, no exhaust, and no emitted light associated with propulsion, that moved at supersonic speeds with no sonic booms or vapor trails. Similar reports later came from naval aviators training over the Atlantic near Virginia.

In the top row of the above matrix, in blue, are the inexplicable kinematics of many UFOs, and in red, the strange absence of behaviors or features such as aerodynamic surfaces, exhaust, heat plumes, etc.

The Xs in the matrix show that an attribute in the top row is theoretically possible with a given type of propulsion, while the question marks denote "may or may not be possible." A blank in the matrix means "can't explain."

In the matrix, where the left column enumerates the different propulsion systems we covered, including in Chapter 2's addendum, there is no single way of pushing or pulling on physical objects that are known–even in theory–that could have all those attributes.

The possibility that comes closest to satisfying all the criteria would be some enhanced version of the Navy's patent on mid-air laser projection (sort of like 3D volumetric holograms, but not precisely holograms) because the air plasmas it creates are essentially massless and can be moved, turned and stopped at breathtaking speeds with no exhaust, no sonic boom, no control surfaces, no anything, really.

But such plasmas are quite luminous and cannot account for the many solid spheroids, Tic Tacs, lozenges, cigars, and other weird shapes not composed of light.

Various forms of photon or directed energy pressure (like the laser levitating disc we showed earlier), which would remove mass from the UFOs, aren't all that attractive either because photon pressure takes a long time to push a sizeable object to any appreciable speed. Also, turning and braking rapidly would be problematic for remote energy beams unless many remote laser beams could hit the object from many directions. Then there's the question: If some UFOs have light sails, where are the sails? Finally, many forms of photon pressure would entail visible photons, either scattered from the craft or observed in route to the craft, but many sightings do not describe such phenomena.

Warp drives "check many boxes" to explain the sightings, but they would undoubtedly have whopping visual signatures, bending spacetime and light the way they do.

Truth in advertising, we did leave out some far-out but theoretically possible concepts, such as the magnetic levitation of UFOs using Earth and water's diamagnetic (repulsive) properties under truly enormous magnetic fields emanating from hypothetical UFOs. Simple math made that look even less viable than warp drives, so we left it out. The fact that UFOs do not seem to affect radio waves and power lines the way astronomically strong magnetic fields would do was another reason for leaving it out.

Ditto for optical tweezer "tractor beams," which can remotely push and pull dielectric (insulating) bodies from a distance. However, the forces involved with optical tweezers are meager compared to moving even ultra-light objects of the reported sizes. 3D volumetric displays using lasers to move glowing dust particles around exist, but the forces required to control UAP-sized objects are prohibitive.

So, where does all this leave us?

You will get an argument from others about whether we exhaustively covered all the possibilities or accurately ruled specific explanations in or out. Still, from where we stand, there is no explanation–**even in theory**–that could explain all the UFO sightings, if indeed the UFOs are artificial objects.

This leaves us (assuming all the relevant reports were truly made honestly, with no fakery or malice) with the following possibilities:

1) The unexplainable UFOs aren't all physical objects, but many are illusions, the equivalent of magic tricks, weird, undiscovered atmospheric effects, or some combination of all the above.
2) The unexplainable UFOs rely on physics that we haven't discovered yet, even in our wildest theories. For example, what if someone, somewhere at some time, figured out how to scoop up dark matter–which is everywhere–and collide it with anti-dark matter (if such a thing exists) to generate lots of propulsive energy but, owing to the strangeness of dark matter, emitting no observable light or heat? No reputable physicist would ever propose such a thing, but hey, it's a good mental picture of far-out physics we haven't discovered yet and shows, by its utter strangeness and improbability, the nature of what we may be dealing with. And, as we pointed out in our intro, some of this weird physics may not be evident now in UFOs because ETs have harnessed it, but because *mother nature* has harnessed it to create meteorological effects that defy all our current ideas about physics.
3) We're back to being Marvin Minsky's cat trying to learn French, and despite how far we push our understanding of physics, we will never solve the mystery.

We do not like option 3) for lots of reasons. There is nothing useful to be gained by dwelling on it, so we will press on from our dive into the human brain and survey of exotic propulsion and take a close look at the possibility of weird atmospheric effects underlying at least some UFO reports.

References

1) https://www.amazon.com/Fundamentals-Quantum-Physics-Engineering-Undergraduate/dp/3642293778

2) https://www.aaro.mil/Portals/136/PDFs/UAP_Reporting_Trends_as_of_20Nov23.pdf?ver=dl2m2HXgCI-MaJ9t5wBmk9Q%3d%3d

3) https://www.archives.gov/news/topics/ufo

4)https://docs.house.gov/meetings/IG/IG05/20220517/114761/HHRG-117-IG05-Transcript-20220517.pdf

5)https://www.armed-services.senate.gov/imo/media/doc/23-31_04-19-2023.pdf

6)https://www.dni.gov/files/ODNI/documents/assessments/FY2023-Consolidated-Annual-Report-UAP-Oct2023.pdf

7)https://smd-cms.nasa.gov/wp-content/uploads/2023/09/uap-independent-study-team-final-report.pdf

8)https://www.nasa.gov/niac-funded-studies/

9)Thorne, Kip (1992). "Closed timelike curves". *General Relativity and Gravitation*: 297.

4. Natural Explanations of UFOs

We have all heard officials explain away UFO sightings as meteors, unusual atmospheric refraction or diffraction effects (bending and scattering of light), electrical discharges, drones, airplanes, rocket launches, satellites, ball lighting, etc.

Before exploring the possibilities of such "natural" explanations, it's worth reviewing statistics on what UFOs look like so we can weigh the odds that something natural and mundane can explain them.

The Pentagon's UFO office (AARO) summary we presented earlier clearly shows that there is no such thing as a typical UFO. Roughly a third of UFOs emit light, another third are orbs or spheres, with the remainder presenting as triangles, discs, cylinders, ovals, squares, etc. A few percent look like Tic Tacs.

So, right off the bat, it's clear that no single natural phenomenon can account for all the sightings.

Atmospheric electrical discharges, exploding powerline transformers, or streaking meteors might account for some of the light-emitting UFOs but can't explain, for example, the Tic Tacs that Naval aviators reported.

Thus, we should consider the whole gamut of natural phenomena, looking for alternative explanations.

But here, we'll only focus on meteorological, astronomical, and other phenomena of mother nature because weather balloons, drones, rockets, airplanes, satellites, runaway kites, mylar party balloons, deorbiting spacecraft, etc., are obvious and uninteresting and have been described ad nausea elsewhere.

Hopefully, in what follows, you'll encounter some possibilities that are new to you and not boring, starting with strange atmospheric optical phenomena.

Optical refraction (bending of light)

The air above us is not uniform but consists of pockets and layers with different temperatures and densities. Just as light rays bend when they move from air into a denser medium, such as a glass lens, they also bend between air regions with different densities in a process called refraction.

When a temperature inversion traps warm air under a layer of cold air, light rays will bend at the cold air/hot air boundary, even to the extent of bending light over the horizon to let you see over the horizon.

This above mirage, called Fata Morgana, makes a ship over the horizon appear to be floating above the horizon. The phenomenon occurs when a thermal inversion has a layer of warm air trap a layer of cold air below it, with a third layer sandwiched between warm and cold layers.

As shown below, this layering creates a ducting effect, very similar to fiber optic waveguides, in which light bends at the warm/cold boundary (due to changing index of refraction at the warm/cold boundary just like the change in refraction that occurs at an air-glass boundary in a prism).

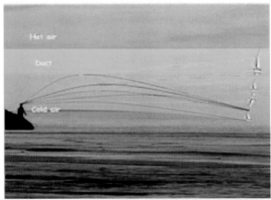

Credit: Brocken Inaglory CC BY-SA 3.0 Wikimedia Commons

When a sailboat is over the horizon, and not ordinarily visible, light rays that would typically go over your head are bent back towards your eye, forming an image or "superior mirage" of the sailboat, which can be both inverted and erect, as indicated in the drawing.

If you've ever seen the sun take much longer than usual to set over the ocean or a flat plain, you've experienced the effect of ducting, which makes the sun appear on the horizon, or just over it, long after it has set.

When the object over the horizon moves, it will make the same movement in mid-air. Some reported UFOs might be from a motorboat, truck, or car zipping along the water or highway, elevated into the sky by ducting.

Below is a different kind of refraction effect, called an inferior mirage, where distant objects appear on or below the ground, as with this illusory image of the sky on a desert floor.

Credit: Public Domain Brocken Inaglory Wikimedia Commons

Refraction at boundaries of different temperature air masses is to blame, as illustrated in this diagram.

The path shown as "a" is the direct liner of sight to a distant object. Refraction causes that path to bend into path "b", which looks like it emerges from the ground along path "c."

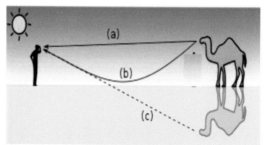

Credit Mike Run CC BY-SA 4.0 Wikimedia Commons

When observers claim a UFO went underwater or ground, they may have seen an inferior image.

An essential feature of atmospheric refraction relevant to UFOs is that convection, turbulence, wind, and other disturbances of air mass can sometimes cause mirage-like images to shimmer, distort, and move around. Fata Morgana mirages are typically not stable but come and go, shimmer, and add or subtract erect and inverted images stacked upon each other over seconds, creating the illusion that objects near the horizon have moved or suddenly disappeared.

Refraction of light also produces Sun Dogs, as shown below, except cold/warm air boundaries are not the culprits. Instead, Sun Dogs appear when plate-shaped ice crystals suspended in the atmosphere capture the sun's rays and bend them back to the eye.

Credit:Gopherboy6956 CCA 2.0 Wikimedia Commons

The same refractive effect also produces Moon Dogs, depicted below.

Credit: Annajohepworth CC0, Wikimedia Commons

Sun and moon dogs can appear in pairs or singly, depending on the time of day and other factors.

Refraction in ice crystals (as opposed to the raindrops that cause rainbows) is also responsible for inverse rainbows called circumzenithal arcs, which bend and disperse (separate colors) white light. Rainbows also bend and disperse light into their color components.

Credit Cdlune1890 Wikimedia Commons

A much more complex phenomenon, Glories, which appear as a projected halo colored on mist or clouds with the sun behind you (giving you a halo, hence the name), also derives, to a certain extent, from the bending of light in atmospheric water droplets, but is quite a bit more complicated to explain (constructive and destructive interference, evanescent waves and so forth, beyond the scope of this book).

Credit Broken Inaglory CC BY-SA 3.0 Wikimedia Commons

The Tangent Arc below occurs when sunlight hits hexagonally shaped ice crystals that are all oriented in the correct direction to bend the sunlight into an arc pattern. Tangent arcs can form around the sun or the moon.

Credit Toddschulte CCA-3 Share Alike 4.0 Wikimedia Commons

Reflection and scattering of light

In addition to bending light also bounces off things, such as light reflecting from these suspended ice crystals below, in what is called a "Sub-sun."

Credit: Brocken Inaglory - CC BY-SA 3.0 Wikimedia Commons

Ice crystals also reflect sunlight in sun pillars, below.

Credit Arvis Geduss CCA 2.0 Wikimedia Commons

The sun reflects off all sorts of things, such as interplanetary dust particles, which, when appropriately illuminated, give a false dawn or Zodiacal light shown below. This light isn't strictly atmospheric because it's scattering from fine particles in space, but it causes the sky to glow, so we'll include it here.

Credit Steven Keys CC BY 4.0 Wikimedia Commons

For completeness, a particular category of scattering is called diffraction, where light scatters in a manner that, due to the wave properties of light, creates patterns of constructive and destructive interference with corresponding, organized patterns of light (where waves constructively interfere) and dark (where light wave destructively interfere).

The alternating light and dark rings around the sun result from diffraction off the edges of dust particles suspended in the air.

Emission of light in the atmosphere through electrical phenomena

You might recall from high school or college science class that electrons orbit the atom's nucleus and occupy discrete orbital bands with different energies. When you heat a light bulb filament, electrons absorb the energy, move up to a higher energy band, and then relax down to their previous band, emitting a photon of light (which is why things glow when you heat them). This light-producing phenomenon, called thermionic emission, explains why coals glow, molten lava glows, etc.

But anything that causes electrons to get excited and then fall from a high-energy state to a lower one will emit a photon.

One famous thing that does this in the atmosphere is lightning. An enormous voltage accumulates when the electrostatic charge on water droplets, particles, and ice crystals in clouds builds up, generating an enormous voltage between the top and bottom of a cloud, or the bottom of the cloud and the Earth. When that voltage exceeds a critical limit, the normally insulating air becomes a conductor, and an enormous current surge results in lightning.

There are many forms of lightning.

Ball lightning below is very rare but can persist much longer than typical lightning and move around erratically.

Credit Joe Thomissen CCA SA 3.0 Wikimedia Commons

Scientists are still determining what causes the weird, rare phenomena. Still, some have proposed dust particles that aggregate into aerosols, accumulate static charge, and discharge when the voltages get high enough.

Lightning can occur at many altitudes, including in the upper atmosphere, as shown on the next page, first with sprites, then blue jets.

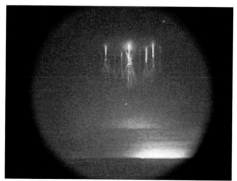

Sprites

Credit: International Gemini Observatory/NOIRLab/NSF/AURA/A. Smith - CC BY 4.0

Blue Jets

ELVES (Emission of Light and Very Low-frequency Perturbations Due to Electromagnetic Pulse Sources) occur when an intense voltage discharges from lightning in one location causing the Ionosphere to light up to 200 kilometers away. The electromagnetic pulse (EMP) of nuclear weapons can also cause ELVES.

Credit: Valter Binotto CCA Wikimedia Commons

ELVES

St. Elmo's Fire is a cousin of lighting caused by build-up and eventual discharge of electrostatic voltages on pointed surfaces, such as the edges of airplanes. The phenomenon appears as white glow on the nose, wing edges and engine housings below.

Credit Anynobody CCA_SA 3.0 Wikimedia Commons

St. Elmo's Fire

Other phenomena can cause atmospheric electrons in the air to do their thing and release stored energy as light. When free electrons and protons from the sun are not deflected by the Earth's magnetic field near the south and north poles, these particles interact with oxygen and nitrogen molecules, emitting light whose color depends on which gas is excited (green or orangish red for oxygen, blue, purple, or red for nitrogen). These lightshows, called Aurora Borealis, occur near the north and south poles. An example is shown below.

Credit: Brocken Inaglory CC BY-SA 3.0 Wikimedia Commons

Aurora Borealis

We previously described STEVE (Strong Thermal Emission Velocity Enhancement), which is like Auroras but can occur at any latitude, not just near the poles. Below is a particularly colorful STEVE from NASA.

Credit: NASA

STEVE

Bioluminescence

Fireflies and related flying insects emit light, such as the dotted green streaks shown below, that, from certain angles, could look like UFOs, especially if, at night, size/distance illusions make them appear further, bigger, and faster than they are.

Credit Jud McCranie - Own work CC BY SA 4 Wikimedia Commons

And below is a firefly up close.

CreditTimo Newton-Syms CCA-SA2.0 Wikimedia Commons

Swamp gas

Also called Ignis Fatuus or will-o-the-wisp, decaying organic matter in swamps and bogs can cause oxidation reactions with phosphine and methane that emit a wispy glow above the ground, which shows up at night.

Here's an artist's rendering with some liberal imagination applied.

Credit: Hermann Hendrich Wikimedia Commons

No photos of Ignis Fatuus (fool's flame) exist, as far as we know, but chemists have reproduced it in the laboratory by combining gases abundant in swamps and bogs.

Clouds

Rare forms of clouds might be mistaken for UFOs. Below is an example of a lenticular cloud.

Credit: Omnisource5 - CC BY-SA 4.0 Wikimedia Commons

If you squint, this lenticular cloud over Dublin, Ireland, could pass for a flying saucer, as could the one below over the Philippines.

Credit: Patryk Reba CC BY-SA 4.0 Wikimedia Commons

Ring-like clouds might also be mistaken for flying saucers.

Credit Maurice D Budden CCA SA 2.0 Wikimedia Commons

Meteors

When small meteors hit Earth's atmosphere, they burn up (unless they survive as meteorites when they hit the ground), creating spectacular shooting stars.

Credit: Navicore Creative Commons Attribution 3.0 Wikimedia Commons

Some meteors, called bolides, can be large and scary when they explode like this one below.

Credit: Thomas Grau, Wikimedia Commons

Artificial objects, like this Soyuz craft, below, reentering the atmosphere, can also light up the sky.

Credit: NASA

Atmospheric effects on radar

Radar data correlating with visual sightings, such as those from the Nimitz carrier group 2004 that reported visual Tic Tacs, can generate misleading returns that masquerade as UFOs when the atmosphere acts on radar energy in unusual ways.

As shown below, the same ducting from inversion layers that bends light also bends radar waves, making objects over the horizon that would otherwise not reflect radar energy, give misleading returns that misrepresent an object's position.

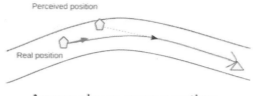

Anomalous propagation

Anyone who has ever seen a radar weather report knows that radar signals can also bounce off rain-laden clouds, as shown below.

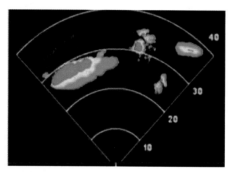

Credit: RicoRico CCA-SA 4.0 Wikimedia Commons

Bragg diffraction, where pockets of alternating air density occur with turbulence, can also generate radar returns called "Radar Angles" in clear air, and yes, these can wobble and move around.

Flying birds can also appear on radar, as illustrated below for a large flock.

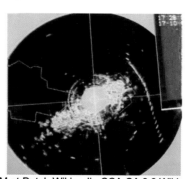

Credit: GerardM at Dutch Wikipedia CCA-SA 3.0 Wikimedia Commons

The charged particles in our Ionosphere can bend radio frequencies for over-the-horizon communication, as anyone who has heard a distant AM radio station can attest.

Credit: Kf4yfd, Noldoaran, Augiasstallputzer~commonswiki CCA-SA 3.0 Wikimedia Commons

Radar frequencies like those on the USS Princeton that detected UAPs in low Earth orbit, then tracked them down to 20,000 feet, use frequencies (like the S-band) that commonly penetrate the Ionosphere and do not reflect from it or bend much when traversing it. But at shallow grazing angles and in conditions of solar storms that turbocharge the Ionosphere, some bending or reflection could place an object in the wrong location at an artificially high altitude, as illustrated in this graphic.

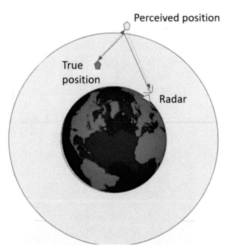

Credit: Kf4yfd, Noldoaran, Augiasstallputzer~commonswiki CCA-SA 3.0 Wikimedia Commons

So, with a radar report that shows an object dropping hundreds of miles from low orbit in seconds with no heat or sonic boom, it is reasonable to ask whether such a flight path truly happened, or weird atmospherics or even radar malfunction are better explanations.

What it all means

After looking at all the weird things that happen naturally in the sky optically and with radars, you can see why some skeptics question the integrity of UFO reports.

To evaluate atmospheric hypotheses, we must apply the same rigor we did in the last chapter with exotic propulsion systems.

This matrix repeats the earlier exercise, focusing only on the verified but unexplained incidents covered in the AARO report.

As before, we lumped many phenomena, such as lightning, into fewer categories (transient "fast" lightning and persistent ball lightning), clouds into just one category, meteors and bolides into another, etc. We did break out several radar anomalies because a few, like ducting, could explain the weird locations and altitudes seen with some UFOs and the appearing/vanishing (which rapidly changing refraction/reflection of radar waves could cause).

As you can see, atmospheric effects and radar anomalies only check a few boxes, mainly because most weather phenomena do not resemble Tic Tacs, spheres, ovals, or the other solid shapes reported. Atmospheric effects also don't move in the required ways. Moreover, most phenomena we covered, including lightning, auroras, and meteors, give off way more light than most UFOs (although 30% of UFOs include lights). And even though both optical ducting and radar ducting can make objects moving on the ground –or at a low altitude-some distance away appear to move in the sky, such movements are still quite distant (over the horizon, by definition), so even a jet zooming over the horizon, or a rocket for that matter, wouldn't appear to move very fast due to the long distances involved.

We put lots of question marks under mirage because pretty much any object can be reimaged through refraction, so, in theory, if someone put a F/A 18 sized Tic Tac over the horizon, ducting could have made it appear in the sky, but again, it would have looked relatively small, and not moved anywhere close to the ways it seemed to move.

	Vanish/appear	Zoom Fast	Turn Quick	Hover long time	Brake Fast	Climb Far Fast	No intake	No exhaust	No moving parts	No light seal	No light or heat	No sonic boom	No distorted air	No Aero shape
Mirage	X	?	?	X			?	?	?	?	?	?	?	?
Short Lightning	X													
Ball Lightning		X	X	?	X	?								
Meteor/Bolide	X	X												
Cloud				X	X									
Biolumin			X		X									
Swamp Gas														
Aurora/STEVE														
St. Elmos Fire														
Radar Ducting	X	?		?										
Radar Birds				?										
Radar Weather				X										
Radar Ionosp.	X	?				X								

Another reason that atmospheric effects don't explain many UFOs is that atmospheric conditions such as lightning weren't present during many sightings, nor were a significant number of sightings at or near the horizon where ducting creates both visual and radar mirages. Also, most UFOs did not emit any light, and those that did emit light were more like point sources of light, not STEVE, ELVES, sprites, blue jets, or ball lightning.

Again, we may not have described every conceivable atmospheric or meteorological effect that observers could mistake for a flying object. Nevertheless, from where we stand, after having gone through this analysis, it appears that Mother Nature can only account for a handful of the sightings, and certainly not those reported by Naval aviators.

So, if you believe our assessment from the last chapter that–probably– no known propulsion system, even in far-out theories, can account for all the sightings, and if atmospheric/meteorological phenomena and radar artifacts also can't explain them, where does that leave us?

That's the exact question we'll take up in the next chapter when we explore the murky world of nefarious human activity that might be behind some UFOs.

5. The faking human hypothesis

Let's start not with the technology of human-made UFOs but with the psychology of humans deploying UFOs in our skies.

The "why" of such hypothetical endeavors is highly pertinent to the "what "and the "how" of UFOs.

For instance, if adversarial humans, say the Chinese or Russians, had made a propulsion breakthrough, would it be likely that that breakthrough would go far beyond our wildest current theories?

We can't say such a thing is impossible, but it would be foolhardy to think it's likely.

No. If humans have leapfrogged us, it's almost certainly in an area we already know is theoretically possible; we just haven't yet learned how to make it practical.

But that high-tech area need not be in propulsion or flight. What if the advanced technology we are dealing with is the technology of deception and fakery, not propulsion?

Ask yourself this: Is it more likely that an adversary has cooked up a way to make us *think* UFOs behave in astonishing ways, or that they have *succeeded* in making UFOs behave in astonishing ways?

Approaching this question, we lean strongly toward the first option because of our many years spent at Disney Imagineering (who designed and built Disney theme parks) and our deep understanding of how, for lack of a better phrase, to fake things.

For instance, we (Eric) once showed the author Tom Clancy a huge floating "Hologram" in Disney's R&D lab that was so convincing that Clancy called for months, pestering Disney to give the fabulous technology to the military for command-and-control displays. Of course, we didn't cave to his demands, but not because the technology was proprietary. We didn't turn the tech over to the military because it was a clever fake that made observers *believe* they saw an honest-to-God 3D animating hologram.

At Disney, we liked to say, "You can appear to walk on water by stepping on stones."

Thus, if an adversary wanted to fool us into believing that UFOs could accomplish virtuoso aerobatic feats and had the equivalent of Disney Imagineering to paint moving holograms in the sky or otherwise "walk on water by stepping on stones" why in the world would they want to do such a thing?

The famous Chinese General Sun Tsu gave a clue in his book, *The Art of War*, when he observed that "All war is deception."

Modern militaries have taken Sun Tsu to heart, spending hundreds of billions on deception.

Remember the Navy patent described in Chapter 1 that uses high-power lasers to draw jets in the air to fool and divert enemy missiles? There's an example for you.

What if the Chinese or Russians (or someone else; we can't only pick on the Chinese and Russians) were testing *their* version of the Navy laser missile countermeasure patent? What better way to test than against the ships, planes, radars, and thermal sensors you may fight someday, say over the Strait of Taiwan?

Another reason adversarial humans might want to fool us into thinking that the impossible is possible is to get us to waste precious time and money that could have gone to more effective capabilities. The Russians are masters of this, practicing the art of what they call *Maskirovka*. For instance, it is rumored that the Russians accidentally on purpose tested a rocket-powered torpedo in Lake Baikal on a cloudless day at the exact moment a US Satellite was flying over to scare the Americans into developing their torpedo and ultra-expensive defenses against it, when in fact, the Russians never intended to take the weapon into production (although they did eventually deploy a slower rocket torpedo, the VA-111 *Shkval*)

Another example of deception is the ultra-classified discipline of electronic warfare (EW), where, let's say, a goal is to make things appear on radar screens that aren't there, or appear in the wrong place, or not appear on the screen at all when they should appear. We won't explain how this is done; we will just casually observe that it might be possible.

Returning to the Navy report of a radar capturing a UAP drop from low Earth orbit to 80,000 feet in seconds, is it possible some form of adversary EW messed with the radar in question?

Hmmm.

Again, why would an adversary do such a thing?

To see how well their EW worked, for one thing.
But another reason might be intimidation. Sometimes, a military will make an adversary believe it can do the impossible so that the adversary will think twice about messing with them or surrender without a fight.

Yet another reason for elaborate fakery could be to test an adversary's capabilities, response times, tactics, etc. What can the enemy sensors see, and at what distance? How does it deploy its forces when threatened? What kind of communication does it use to coordinate responses? All beneficial information if you ever intend to fight that adversary.

But you don't have to go to that dark place necessarily; sometimes, an adversary might want to learn what another military does so that they can copy them.

Finally, think about what happened in the US in the last year. UAPs are so much in the news, with Congressional Hearings, the recent release of masses of data on UAPs mandated by Congress, NASA reports, etc., that the idea UFOs are real has taken root in the US like never before.

As a result, if our military ever does go to war with country X, who is faking impossible UFO flight patterns, our military may take them seriously if they see these fakes on or near the battlefield and waste precious resources tracking them, chasing them, and shooting at them. Just look at all the decoys used by Russia and Ukraine right now to see how such a scenario could play out.

In this context, the fake UFOs, especially those popping up over our flight training ranges, could be what is called a "shaping" operation, gradually shaping our perception to take them seriously so that, when things get serious, the UFOs will be a significant asset on the battlefield, along with other tools of deception such as EW.

So, yes, we can easily imagine why someone might want to fake UFOs. But then, how might they do this?

Faking UFOs

We mentioned the Disney principle of "walking on water by stepping on stones," not because Disney is in the deception business but because it is in the storytelling business.

The essence of all good theme park illusions, and stage magic tricks for that matter, is storytelling. That's why Disney theme park rides and shows all have pre-shows to give you the back story that motivates the journey you are about to take. Also, why do stage magicians go to great lengths in their setup: for instance, before the trick, having an audience member testify that a glass is empty, a metal ring has no breaks, etc.?

The reason is simple: Storytelling points your brain in the direction the storyteller wishes it to go. The story can be simple: "I intend to cut my assistant in two pieces." or "I will make her disappear."

Our brains see what they expect to see and don't see what they don't expect to see, and stories tell the brain what to expect and, perhaps more importantly, what to unconsciously ignore. When you get right down to it, illusionists do not tell a story so much, as they cleverly persuade the brains of their audiences to tell those same brains a story.

Knowing this, if someone gave us the task of faking UFOs at sea with impossible performance envelopes, we'd start by trying to understand the audience for our fakery to craft a story that was likely to make that audience tell themselves a fable where we got them to see what we wanted them to see while ignoring what we *didn't* want them to see.

Stage magic on a grand scale

When faking UFOs, "understanding the audience" means taking stock of how many observers there would be, what their sight lines would be, and what kinds of sensors they would have deployed, to name just a few parameters.

Meticulous attention to detail must be taken at this stage because all good illusions depend upon rigid control of conditions necessary to make the illusion work: to place all the metaphorical "stones" in the right places right under the metaphorical water so that you can metaphorically walk on that metaphorical water.

This means, for example, that you would only attempt the illusion on days when weather conditions, the number of observers, and viewing geometries were optimal. You might construct your UFOs from radar-transparent material to make it difficult for the "audience" to determine their distance from the objects. Or, if you had lots of money and nearby EW gear, you might mess with those radars in just the right way at the right time.

As with a good theme park ride or a magician's setup, there would be some backstory that points the minds of observers in the right direction.

For instance, one way to create the illusion of a big object moving very fast, far away is to start conditioning the audience with moving objects that are, in fact, very far away, say 5-10 miles away. Those objects would have a specific size, shape, and flight pattern. Then, focus the audience's (say, Naval observers on training exercises) attention on the distant objects by doing something dramatic, like blowing one of the distant objects up, that would be sure to divert their attention.

Precisely at that moment when attention is elsewhere, stealthily introduce another object or two, with the same angular size and shape as the distant objects but much closer to the observers (the objects would be much smaller than the far distant decoys, but at closer range, appear the to be the same size).

The naked eye has poor stereovision beyond 50 feet, so it could easily be fooled into believing they are just as far away as all the other identical-looking objects when it first notices the closer objects. At first, the objects would move at the same slow angular rate as their more distant cousins, reinforcing the illusion that they were far away.

But then, the close objects (say, high-performance drones disguised as Tic Tacs) could zip around as fast as they are able, shocking the observers into thinking big objects far away had moved impossibly fast because that motion would be perceived to have occurred very far away. Recall the example of a frisbee tossed across your sight line right before you. If your brain believed that the Frisbee was miles away, that velocity would seem impossible (and the Frisbee diameter enormous).

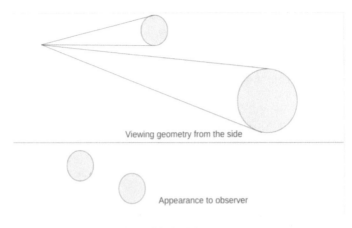

Viewing geometry from the side

Appearance to observer

Far & Big   Close & Small

In this example, you would not put on your show on a hazy day where intervening haze would give away your ruse by blurring the distant objects more
than the closer ones. You would pay attention to many other details, like
keeping the viewing time of the fast-moving sphere short, choosing favora-
ble paint schemes for the spheres, picking a day with choppy seas if needed
to create masking radar clutter, etc., etc.

When observers of this illusion tell the story you have gotten them to weave
inside their heads, they'd say: "First some weird spheres appeared on the
horizon moving about, then one blew up and immediately after another took
off like a bat out of hell to escape the same fate." A simple story with a beginning, middle, and end that made a certain kind of sense (remember, the
brain makes sense of things by presenting you a reality where A caused B
caused C even when A most certainly did not cause B)

Because the audience did not see this spectacle repeat on many different
days, under different weather and viewing conditions, they could quickly
conclude that it could have happened on any day when the illusion might
only work one or two days out of the year.

The illusionists cheated, big time, but that's not the story the observers will remember (and report).

Before moving on, it's worth dwelling on how one could disguise a drone to look like a sphere, egg, Tic Tac, oval, or other non-drone-like shape that shows no control surfaces, no engines or means of propulsion, and no visible exhaust.

The most crucial point, as always, is to let the observer's brain do most of the heavy lifting for you, filling in information where there is none while ignoring critical information that *is* there if you only pay close attention, which almost no one ever does.

With a sphere, the simplest way to enlist the brain as an ally is to know where your observer is and always keep the openings for the propeller or ducted fan (jet) hidden from that point of view. A sphere could have an opening on top to suck in air that was covered with a mesh painted the same color as the sphere body, so from a distance, the air intake would not be visible. With any conventional propulsion system, there would need to be openings underneath to expel air or exhaust gases. Yet, knowing where your observers are, you could take great care to hide those openings from their line of sight, just as a magician hides the back of their hand when they make a coin magically appear.

If all that observers can see is a sphere, as with the illusory square in Chapter 2, their brains will fill in what they don't see and tell themselves, "That's a perfect sphere."

To guard against the possibility that someone might see holes in the bottom of the sphere that allow forced air out, you could mount bright lights that would prevent the eye from seeing any details in the bottom of the sphere (just as you can't see much on the road looking into the sun). Incidentally, a fair number of UFOs do have bright lights like this.

In this sphere below, due to the sun angle and shading, it's tough to see the four small black openings in the bottom, especially if we turned on a blinding light at the bottom.

But an honest-to-God 360-degree sphere with no masking lights could fly using a few more techniques from the magicians' bag of tricks.

With ultra-stiff, lightweight composites, it is now possible to mount drone motors/propellers quite a distance from the drone's body on ultrathin but with strong, camouflaged struts.

Even in daylight, sky-colored thin struts are challenging and impossible to see at night. And whirring propellers themselves are invisible while spinning, even in daylight.

Finally, the observers' attention will automatically fixate on the magically floating and moving sphere, not the disguised struts and motors. This has been proven in multiple entertainment venues using this gag successfully.

Motors and propellers can also be small and inconspicuous if the sphere is Styrofoam and filled with helium for buoyancy (although it can't move very fast because of a need to counter sustained upward lift).

A variation of the thin-strut-hide-the-motors gag is to mount the light Styrofoam (or helium-filled) sphere on a single thin black strut from a small quadcopter or octocopter a fair distance *above* the sphere. This time, in the rare event observers look up at the disguised lifting mechanism, you can mount a bright light on top of the sphere to blind observers to fine details. The picture below illustrates the single strut concept.

We are using high technology to fake even *higher* technology.

So far, we have only talked about clever, low-tech use of drones.

But if you are a nefarious human with deep pockets, strong motivation, and access to technology that your target audience doesn't know exists, you can really mess with your target's heads.

Recall two phenomena we covered earlier: high-powered lasers and atmospheric ducting.
Believe it or not, it's possible to change the atmosphere to create an optical waveguide in the air. This kind forms mirages and anomalous radar propagation using a high-powered laser.

This technique is called "self-focusing" because the high-powered laser heats the air through which it travels, creating a hot air/cool air boundary and forming an artificial duct akin to a fiber optic. With such a duct, a laser beam that would otherwise expand as it traveled from its source would keep some of its original compactness and high power even at a long distance. And, if atmospheric turbulence threatens to distort the beam, another technology, called adaptive optics phase conjugation, can pre-distort the laser wavefront to compensate for atmospheric distortion, further increasing the distance over which ducting occurs. In case you wanted to know, the Russians invented phase conjugation of lasers.

The laser in question need not be in a visible band, tipping your hand to an unsuspecting observer that you are seriously messing with the atmosphere. Invisible CO_2 pulsed lasers work well to form self-focused laser ducts because air molecules absorb the 10.5-micron wavelengths of CO_2 lasers very well.

The net effect would be to create invisible ducts in the sky that could, for example, make an object like a sphere mysteriously appear and quickly disappear, as if powered by a space drive straight out of science fiction.

As with the sphere illusion, we (nefarious high-tech humans) take great care to control the "stage," picking just the right moment," audience, weather conditions, and so forth.

In this case, we place two lasers on the ground, aiming their beams to intersect in the path of an unsuspecting pilot. Where the two laser beams intersect, a bent, refracting duct can form under just the right atmospheric conditions (lack of wind or turbulence). With a bent duct in the air an object placed near the origin of one beam, behind a beam splitter that directs light from the object along the optical path of the laser, will appear as a virtual image floating in the sky, as illustrated below. The artificial mirage is formed when some of the light from that object "leaks" around the corner (faint, bent dotted line) of the intersection of two artificial atmospheric ducts (even though most of the light from the object will head off into space).

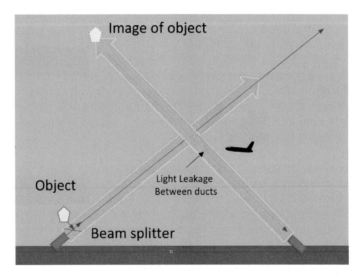

Motorized mirrors move the paths of the two beams to track the hapless pilot if desired. When the aircraft enters the ducting zone, such an arrangement would create the illusion of an object appearing ahead of and above the pilot when, in fact, the physical object was on or near the ground. Our high-tech illusionists could make the object appear to vanish simply by turning off one beam or moving the object out of the duct formed by one laser.

Poof! A UFO that suddenly appears and disappears!

By moving the two laser beams, the image can pop up in different places, like the Phi-Phenomenon moving bowling ball, appearing to move at "impossible" speeds.

Yes, it is very tricky to get some light from the object to leak around the corner, as it were, and it could be hard to get your head around the esoteric concept if you're not into optics, but the ducting gag could work under the right conditions, especially, if the adversaries are experts in directed energy and adaptive optics (hint: the Russians are).

The difficulty of getting one's mind around such technology is a massive advantage for nefarious humans desiring to fool other humans. Who would ever think of such a bizarre thing?

Before the lady-cut–in-half magic trick, who would ever have thought of cramming and contorting two women into shallow tables?

The essence of illusion, deception, and magic is to pull something off that the audience could not imagine, like creating artificial mirages with laser beams.

Speaking of laser beams, remember the Navy patent on creating a 3D airborne image of a fighter plane to spoof enemy missile seekers?

Here's more detail on how nefarious humans could deploy such a thing to fake UFOs with impossible flight patterns.

When a pulsed, ultra-high power laser beam focuses to a point with a lens, the concentration of energy is so extreme that it rips electrons away from air molecules, forming a glowing, hot plasma.

By changing the focal distance at which the plasma forms and steering the laser with mirrors precisely how entertainers present laser light shows, a three-dimensional volumetric display can be created from just one laser and moved around in the air, forming any 3D shape.

The graphic below on the left depicts a high-power CO_2 laser whose beam is focused through a lens and directed by a motorized steering mirror to form a point of hot plasma. The lens and mirror can rapidly move, changing both the focal point (and distance in 3D space) of the laser and the angular position of the plasma, as shown on the right, where both the lens and steering mirror moved to place the plasma in a different location.

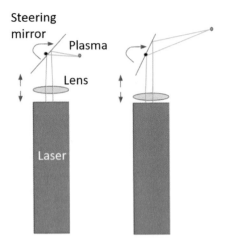

Each plasma is a 3D pixel (or Voxel for "volume element") that a computer graphics system can form into arbitrary shapes through control of the lens and mirror, such as this geometric figure below. Here, we show only one steering mirror that allows the plasma voxel to be painted anywhere in a flat plane, but adding a second mirror enables the plasma to show up anywhere in 3 dimensions.

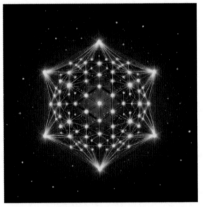

We (Eric) have built such displays in the past while developing indoor fireworks, which sadly, never presented a live show because audiences tend to freak out when the air over their heads catches fire.

The polyhedron on the preceding page can move around in three dimensions just as quickly as the laser beams in light shows, so if someone wanted to fake impossible aerobatics, it wouldn't be difficult.

Radar can be faked, too

We can't say much here about how Electronic Warfare (EW) can make objects pop up on radar displays and appear to move in jaw-dropping ways except to point out that it would be unwise to take odds against some nefarious humans doing exactly such a thing to fake UFO radar signatures.

But we can talk about some high-tech, starting with the laser plasmas we just described which, with some radars, can reflect radar energy and show up on radar screens.

Incidentally, hot plasmas would also show up strongly on infrared imagers, which is how they spoof infrared missile seekers.

Another technology is switchable mirrors, which go from transparent to reflective in response to an applied voltage. Some use metal–like liquid crystals, while others, called reversible electrochemical mirrors, use a clear fluid in which silver ions are in solution, which forms a reflective mirror on a special electrode when the correct voltage is applied to that electrode. Below on the left is the mirror in mirror mode; on the right is the same mirror in transparent mode.

 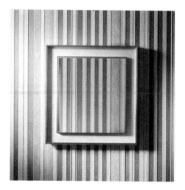

Switchable mirrors will also change how much they reflect radar waves between reflective and transparent modes, especially for radars with shorter wavelengths, enabling airborne objects covered with such mirrors to appear to blink on and blink off. Objects covered with switchable mirrors can appear and suddenly disappear or, if deployed on multiple balloons or other radar transparent air vehicles, through the magic of the Phi Phenomenon illusion, appear to be a single object moving impossibly fast through the air.

This graphic simulates three airborne objects at three distances away from the radar.

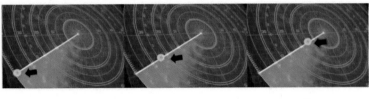

Far   Closer   Very close

The yellow blip represents the radar return from an aircraft-like object, where distance from the center of the scan indicates range-from-radar and the angle of the radar sweep (white line) indicates bearing of the target from the radar. On the left, the blip is at the extreme limit of the radar's range, on the far right, the target is near the radar. If three objects, such as radar transparent weather balloons carried switchable mirrors, and the mirrors turned on and off with the correct timing, a radar "phi phenomenon" would fool the radar operator into thinking there was a single fast-moving target instead of three stationary objects whose radar reflectivity turned on and off.

The sky's the limit for faking humans

Writing coaches advise authors to write what they know, and we know optics and special effects, so those are mostly the types of UFO skullduggery we have cooked up to illustrate how nefarious humans might go about faking UFOs.

But there are many more possibilities, especially if you embrace the premise that adversaries could have leapfrogged us in many different areas and are using those advances to pull the wool over our eyes.

If you're skeptical that someone could secretly blow past us (The USA) in technology, history shows such skepticism is unwarranted. Here's a short list of nasty surprises we've had in this regard:

- Sputnik (Russia shocked us with its first satellite)
- First human in space (and a Russian orbited when we could only go up and down)
- Atomic bomb (Russia got one far faster than we thought possible)
- Stealth technology (we got the idea from Russian scientists)
- Lasers (we got the idea from Russian Valentin Fabricant in the 1930s)
- Hypersonic weapons (Russia and China have them, we don't)
- Russian Radio Frequency spy technology (see our book *The Spy in Moscow Station* and our articles in *PsychologyToday* on Havana syndrome)

The US never had a monopoly on high tech, and whatever lead we did have is slipping away as the democratization of technology (thanks to AI, automation, wide availability of supercomputers, etc.) dramatically lowers the barrier to entry to conducting big science.

With all of that said, we'll end this chapter the way we started it. With a question: Is it more likely that sophisticated technology is faking UFOs, or making UFOs *genuinely* do the things that have been reported?

We'll resurrect our sturdy matrix once again to cross-check different fakery techniques against the unexplained reports from the Navy to answer that question. The caveat is that we've left off leapfrog technologies we can't guess at, which are numerous if history is a guide (ergo, the blank rows).

Here, we speculate that, as before, plasmas might explain several reports, but not most of them, which lack lights.

Theoretically, optical illusions, such as the Phi Phenomenon and those created by size/distance/velocity confusions, could explain all visual sightings (so all the boxes are checked). Still, where radar, thermal, video, and eyewitness reports agree, optical illusions alone cannot fully explain what happened if such illusions were practical on a grand scale.

Although masking engines, air intakes, air exhausts, propulsion, and moving control surfaces, the drone gags we described can only achieve the altitudes, speeds, and accelerations reported if observers got the distance to UFOs very wrong. Thus, drones could account for some reports, especially where objects moved slowly.

But far from all the reports.

Similarly, laser ducting (no one has ever done it this way, to our knowledge, even though it's theoretically possible) could explain some visual reports but, by itself, could not replicate multi-sensor reports. The same would be true if fakers waited for natural ducts to form to pull off UFO magic.

Switchable mirrors, especially deployed on multiple separated platforms and cleverly deployed, could fake out some radars, but not the fighter aircraft radars that locked onto moving visual targets.

We're not sure what EW can do to radars, and if we did know, we wouldn't tell you, so we've left many question marks there. EW alone could not create the visual/video/thermal image reports.

	Plasmas	Optical Illusions	Drones	Laser Ducting	Switch Mirrors (Radar)	EW
No Aero shape	X	X		X		
No distorted air	X	X		X		
No sonic boom	X	X		X		
No light or heat		X	X	X		
No light sail	X	X	X	X		
No moving parts	X	X		X		
No exhaust	X	X	X	X		
No intake	X	X	X	X		
Climb Far Fast	X	X	?	X	X	?
Brake Fast	X	X	?	X	X	?
Hover long time	X	X	X	X	?	?
Turn Quick	X	X	?	X	X	?
Zoom Fast	X	X	?	X	X	?
Vanish/appear	X	X		X	X	?

So, once again, we've arrived at the assessment that if nefarious humans are faking UFOs using some combination of optical illusions, magic tricks, and high-tech or clever and timely use of the atmosphere, we can't understand how they are pulling off the feat, especially with sightings such as those reported by the Navy in 2004.

If at least some of the UFO reports aren't fakes, aren't optical illusions, and aren't using science-fiction propulsion, what could they be?

That's what the next chapter is all about.

6.   The non-faking human hypothesis

Faking ultra-high-performance UFOs would be far easier than making UFOs perform in ways that have been reported. However, we can't rule out the possibility that some, or even all the "legitimate" UFO sightings, such as those described in the Pentagon's AARO report and similar reports by the Director of National Intelligence and NASA, have a human origin and are not fakes.

By not fakes, we mean the mysterious phenomena accelerate, zoom, stop, climb, loiter for 8 hours, and turn in "impossible ways" while exhibiting no apparent means of propulsion, control surfaces, exhaust, or disturbances of air, and sometimes water, near them.

We won't repeat the possibilities already covered for advanced propulsion. Instead, we will focus here on the possible motivations of humans behind the "genuine" (non-faked) UFOs and our assessment of what the human origins of the phenomena/objects most likely represent.

Motivations: "Normal operations"

Thus far, we have theorized that adversary humans might create elaborate ruses for shaping perception, intimidation, harassment, or gathering intelligence.

But we must consider that, at least concerning UFOs reported over the US, our government is behind some of the incidents.

For instance, statistics on where UFOs appear in the US show that quite a few occur near test or training flight ranges that the public does not *know* are flight ranges but not around air bases and airports. Civilians may only report a few UFOs near airports because they expect things to move in the sky there, but civilians report most UFOs around areas not well known as air training or test ranges.

One such area was Groom Lake, Nevada, better known as Area 51.

Of course, another interpretation of the unusual frequency of reports near flight ranges is that military pilots (who are generally deemed credible), by definition, spend a lot of time around such ranges, are one of the chief sources of reports on UAPs, implying a sample bias for reporting around flight ranges (because that's where the pilots spend the most time).

Experimental aircraft with weird shapes, such as the Frisbee-shaped F-117 Stealth fighter and Flying Wing B2, tend to be initially evaluated in remote areas, away from prying eyes. Still, occasionally, civilians spot and report them. The recent proliferation of drones of diverse shapes, sizes, and flight patterns, and the presumable test of military versions of these drones over remote ranges, has created even more opportunities for reporting unusual activity, even by US Government observers who are unaware of advanced development and testing going on in certain places. The military routinely compartmentalizes sensitive information, so that even individuals with high-level security clearances might be kept in the dark about sensitive programs for which they have no "need to know."

Rail guns may also be behind a few sightings, especially given that such projectiles can maneuver with tiny, hard-to-see fins, without any visible en-gine or exhaust, because rail gun projectiles can accelerate to around 15,000 MPH with a big boost from an external power source.

And, relevant to the Navy patent on laser plasma countermeasures, perhaps someone saw and reported Naval tests of such a system. This possibility is worth considering because fast-moving plasmas can zip around in the astounding manner that some UFOs have exhibited, far beyond the perfor-mance of even the most advanced aircraft known.

That said, there are extraordinary flying craft that the Government has acknowledged fly in very unexpected ways.

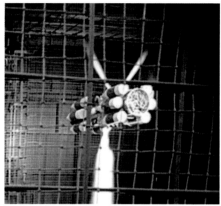
Credit: US DOD Missile Defense Agency

Above is a photo of a "Multi Kill Vehicle" (MKV), developed for the Missile Defense Agency, presumably to destroy hostile objects in space or the upper atmosphere.

It has rocket motors aimed in 6 different directions (think faces of a cube) to hover, move up/down, right/left, and forward/back with no wings or flight control surfaces. Videos of this object look very strange, as the rockets pulse on and off extremely rapidly, appearing from a distance to be fast-blinking lights.

The flight performance of the MKV has not been made public, but from the design, it could indeed hover, go up and down, zoom, brake, and turn quite quickly. Not with the astonishing G's reported for some UFOs, but presumably brisk enough to "kill" whatever fast-moving threats.

Up close, it bears no resemblance to Tic Tacs, spheres, or triangles, but it, or something like it, might have been behind a few sightings.

Or the DARPA Long Shot remote missile launch platform (below), if you squint and look at it from an angle where the wings aren't prominent, could look like a Tic Tac.

Credit: DARPA

And yes, once upon a time, our Government built and tested a real flying saucer that someone, even an unwitting military pilot, could have seen and reported.

Credit US Air Force

In their recent reporting, AARO, NASA, and the Intelligence Community factored in knowledge about classified flight programs now and in the past that could explain some of the sightings. But, having worked in the vast bureaucracy of the US National Security apparatus, we (Eric) observe that one can never assume the right hand knows what the left is doing. Perhaps AARO, NASA, and even the Intelligence Community have been kept intentionally in the dark, or, more likely, information on some obscure compartments was overlooked, forgotten, misplaced, or outright lost.

In the intelligence world, we used to say, "When trying to understand someone's behavior and the two most likely causes are malice and incompetence, always choose the latter." To be charitable, bureaucratic inertia is a softer way of explaining why, without malice or cover-up, the Government itself may not know everything the Government knows, if you know what we mean.

Motivations: not so normal operations

Here is where we start to wade into what some might consider conspiracy theories. We acknowledge the adage, "Just because you're paranoid doesn't mean they aren't out to get you."

While the most likely scenario is that recent government reports and statements about UAPs are accurate and genuine, if less than 100% are forthcoming, certain factoids may have been missed because they were *meant* to be missed.

For instance, what if one part of the Government has secretly developed something in a deep, dark, classified compartment and wants to test it on an unsuspecting *other* part of the Government over a training range? Where flight safety is a concern, it's doubtful that Organization A would willfully jeopardize the life of pilots in Organization B by distracting them in flight or causing them to make radical changes to their flight paths. But one couldn't say such a thing was impossible, mainly where intense historical rivalries between Organizations A and B existed.

Army, Navy, and Air Force sometimes do not get along, especially where the dividing line between their missions gets blurry, as with air defense. And the CIA, which operates its aircraft, has a culture of long-standing antagonism towards the military. Not all CIA officers feel this way, but more than you might imagine. And some folks in uniform return the favor.

If you will, all regular bureaucratic turf fights could occasionally blossom into UFO reports when one actor decides the mess with another—supposedly friendly—actor.

And we must acknowledge that despite laws that prohibit the Government from lying to the public, it's conceivable that AARO, NASA, and the Intelligence community have claimed ignorance about the ultimate sources of UAP's, when in fact they know exactly what is going on.

Think about it. Suppose, at first, the Pentagon AARO group genuinely didn't understand what was behind many UAPs, then suddenly discovered the truth. Disbanding the office would signal to the world that they had gotten the answers they were looking for, which would not typically be something they would want to advertise, at least right away. For instance, if they discovered our adversaries were behind the UFOs, they wouldn't want those adversaries to know that we knew. In such a scenario, do you think the Pentagon would keep AARO going, issuing reports and professing genuine ignorance? They'd almost have to behave that way.

Or, going way out in left field, if the military did stumble across ETs, what are the odds they'd initially sit on the information while they tried to figure out the best way to respond?

All of which means the truth may be "in there" somewhere in the bowels of the Pentagon or CIA, and we're never going to learn about it, despite the recent Congressional mandate for wide release of information on UAPs.

And maybe, like most Government secrets, there would be very legitimate reasons for the secrecy, as would be the case with discoveries about foreign human actors messing with us. Other valid reasons for the Government to keep what they know secret include protecting sources and methods of classified collection systems that might have captured UFO activity or revealing to the adversary what we know and don't know about UFOs that has military ramifications. If we were certain, for instance, that UFOs were flying craft that used anti-matter drives, we would try to figure out how to do the same before letting anyone else know that such propulsion was feasible.

Foreign actors

For many of the same reasons foreign actors might want to fake UFOs, they might also want to fly real, super high-performance aircraft in our skies, especially over military test and training ranges.

Testing the responses of our sensors, weapons, and aircraft would be one motivation, intimidation another, and Maskirovka yet a third. When the Russians –reputedly– tested their hypervelocity rocket torpedo, the prototype was real enough but not presumably deemed by the Russians to ever be practical for full-scale production. An adversary could show us some super-duper prototype to get us to panic and waste money trying to defend against or replicate it.

None of which answers the question, how could foreign adversaries make UAPs fly the way they do?

As the preceding matrices demonstrated, we don't know.

But we can still rough out the crude edges of what might be happening, taking our best guesses at probabilities.

One such informed guess would be that the UFOs, however they work, are unmanned. Humans can tolerate only 9 Gs for brief periods, but the plus 50 Gs exhibited by many UFOs would squish humans into pink mush, tear them apart, or both. The "objects" could be remote-controlled or flown by AIs. Still, it's tough to imagine any human surviving those kinds of accelerations (if the accelerations are not illusory).

Another informed guess would be that if foreign actors are flying UFOs, the propulsion systems are not warp drives, tractor beams, levitating magnetic fields, or any other exotic, theoretically not impossible means of moving through the air. Even though the lack of apparent exhaust, rocket plumes, moving parts control surfaces, and flight vectoring imply the existence of something exotic under the hood, it is more likely, though not sure, that more conventional propulsion systems are being used and hidden.

For instance, what if a craft had zillions of tiny thrusters, each venting exhaust through a small opening in a mesh screen? From a distance, the mesh screen would look solid (think of the half-tone coloring in comic books, which only looks like isolated dots of color when you magnify them). The craft could turn without control surfaces like the Multi Kill Vehicle, with thrusters venting in all six directions in a precisely controlled way.

Earlier, we mentioned that electrodynamic and magneto dynamic generation of airflows is possible by first ionizing atmospheric oxygen and nitrogen and then propelling those ions in desired directions with electrostatic or magnetic fields. Deploying such ion-based systems near masking screens could preserve needed laminar airflow from drone propellers, even when a masking screen covering the bottom of the craft would usually disrupt downward airflow and severely compromise lift. This ionization produces light, but sunlight might overwhelm such light in the daytime.

It's also possible that, with UFOs moving fast and pilots being distracted, foreign-made UFOs have control surfaces and even visible engines that are not obvious in rapid flybys or blurry video images.

These ideas still can't explain the extraordinary performance of some UFOs, but they could be helpful in eventually getting to the ultimate truth.

A third informed guess, growing out of the remote-control hypothesis, is that the foreign actors in question who might be behind UFOs are using communication channels to and from the objects that are extremely difficult to detect (because no such communications have been reported). Infrared lasers could accomplish this, or some clever way of masking radio frequency signals to "look" like routine radio signals from satellites, microwave relays, or even search radars. In *The Spy in Moscow Station*, we detail how the Russians, 40 years ago, used such masking techniques for their bugs in our Moscow embassy to avoid detection.

One caveat to this guess is the curious mention, never explained, in the Pentagon 2023 AARO UAP report of radio "signatures" of 1-3 GHZ and 8-10 GHZ (Microwaves) associated with "typical" UAPs. Whether those radio signatures are simply present in the environment or emitted from the UAPs is unclear.

We also suggest that when fast-accelerating UAPs are physical objects (vs. plasmas or some optical phenomena), very lightweight materials, including propulsion and attitude control systems, make up those objects. Our speculation goes back to the good old F=MA equation: when you see high A, one explanation is low M relative to the amount of F applied. Of course, removing all propulsion from the craft with a rail gun or remote photon beam would be the ultimate way to keep M low.

A final guess about potential foreign actors who might be responsible for UFOs is that whoever is flying the mysterious UFOs has a high tolerance for risk. Sooner or later, a UFO is bound to crash, fail to self-detonate as planned, and be recovered by the US, or cause an accident, or be tied to its source with uncomfortable repercussions, including loss of advanced technology.

And, while it's true the Chinese have been known to fly perilously close to our military aircraft to intimidate them in international air space and take other risks in pursuit of foreign policy goals, the ultimate risk takers are the Russians. They make a lot more too-close-for-comfort approaches to our fighters than the Chinese do, shoot down commercial airlines (like Korean Flight 007 or the Dutch plane over Ukraine) when it suits their interests, zap our foreign service officers with microwaves (Moscow embassy and probably the Havana syndrome) and engage in bad behaviors towards NATO and US personnel routinely. So, if foreign actors are behind some or most UFOs, particularly those involving dangerous encounters in our military ranges, the most obvious culprit would be the Russians.

None of which excludes the possibility that neutral or even friendly countries are flying in our skies and test ranges, or for that matter, private companies or individuals.

But the betting odds say that if non-US government actors are responsible, the list of suspects is very short, with two big Asian powers —one in particular—at the top.

It's important to emphasize that all these guesses are just that, guesses based on our assessment of probabilities, which, of necessity, are based on experience and limited data.

Nevertheless, despite the risk that we turn out to be wrong, we wanted to advance some informed guesses that might lead to deeper insights about the origins of UFOs.

Like the Russians, we don't mind taking some risks.

Speaking of risks, we will now go way out on a limb and do what no Government agency has dared to do: engage in a serious discussion of the possibility that ETs are behind some of the UFO reports.

7.   Non-Human Origins of UFOs

So much has been written about aliens visiting Earth, not to mention movies and TV shows on the subject, along with interviews with people who claim to have been abducted by aliens, that it is a big challenge to offer any new insights.

For instance, we could talk about hints that ETs exist from SETI's "Wow" signal (one unexplained deep space radio transmission that might have come from ETs), from NASA's spectrographic analysis of atmospheres of exoplanets showing traces of organic molecules that are building blocks of life, or astrobiology experiments on the emergence of life on Earth suggesting that life could be common in the cosmos. Still, we won't go into all that (much) because we have nothing new to add.

If you discount reports of alien sightings and abductions (which we do based on unconvincing evidence), the only evidence–if you can call it evidence–that ETs are behind some UFOs is all negative. In our matrices we rule out human and natural causes of a few UFOs, which could lead some people to conclude the only remaining possibility is ET's.

But are ETs the only viable alternative to human or natural causes.?

When we see other people interested in UFOs lay out all the possibilities, as we have in this book, we get the uneasy feeling that something is missing because logic and science do not necessarily constrain the valid options to the extent there are possibilities we can't imagine. And our imaginations, like that of an intelligent cat attempting to learn French, are, for sure, limited.

For instance, a typical "exhaustive" list of possibilities for UFOs looks something like this:

1)   Misidentification of natural phenomena (meteors, weird atmospheric effects)
2)   Misidentification of human activity (balloons, airplanes, rockets, intentional fakes)
3)   Outright lies by UFO reporters
4)   Ultra-advanced, secret human capabilities

5) ETs
6) Some combination of the above

The list seems exhaustive, but is it?

Some people would argue that we have left off supernatural explanations: Signs from God, ghosts, demonic apparitions, and so forth.

As scientists, we carefully avoid talking about the supernatural because there is no scientific way of disproving faith-based ideas, so those ideas aren't subject to the scientific method, and we won't discuss them further.

But here's where things get tricky: Arthur C Clarke correctly pointed out, *"Any technology that is sufficiently advanced will be indistinguishable from magic."* Thus, supernatural (magical) alternatives for UFOs might someday be scientifically verifiable.

An example of another "magical" possibility not on the "exhaustive' list

Let's face it: If you believe our earlier assessments that there are no explanations for some of the UFO reports, then the ultimate truth, from today's perspective, will seem to have a vanishingly small probability of being viable.

And suppose you also feel in your guts that the "exhaustive" lists of alternatives, such as the one we just presented, might be missing something. In that case, this section is for you, if you don't mind experiencing what it feels like to imagine the unimaginable.

But if you're uncomfortable traveling up to the boundary of what constitutes science, you could skip this section and go right to the end, where the ideas are far out but closer to the scientific mainstream.

Here's an example of a possibility at the borders of our imagination based on the work of scientists such as James Lovelock, creator of the Gaia theory, and Physicist Adam Frank and colleagues at the University of Rochester. The possibility we are about to discuss is like Arthur C. Clark's "magic," with one important difference: Biology not technology drives the science behind the apparent "magic".

Suppose a planet, such as the Earth, is an intelligent entity made up of all the individual living organisms that comprise it, in the same way, our consciousness is made up of individual neurons that give rise to consciousness.

Consciousness, motivation, intent, and other intelligent processes are emergent properties of extensive collections of separate but communicating entities, so is it possible that, on a much larger scale, all of the separate but communicating living entities on Earth combine in some way to produce a super-intelligence for the Earth itself (or for that matter, any planet with life on it).

One of the original proponents of this idea was atmospheric scientist John Lovelock.

Lovelock noticed several phenomena that made no sense, ultimately leading him to the radical conclusion that the Earth behaves as a single living being despite having roughly 9 million different species of living organisms. (1,2).

Here is what made no sense to Lovelock:

- The salinity (saltiness) of the oceans has remained at about 3.4% over a billion years, despite runoff from rivers that continuously adds salt to the oceans from land erosion.
- The average temperature on Earth has been relatively stable over the last billion years despite a 30-40% increase in solar radiation striking the planet.
- Oxygen in the atmosphere climbed from almost nothing 2.5 billion years ago to 21% 600 million years ago and has stayed at that level ever since.

Like all good scientists, Lovelock looked for the simplest explanation for the odd behavior of the atmosphere and oceans. He concluded that a single force acted like a thermostat to stabilize environmental conditions on Earth. According to Lovelock, this force exerted negative feedback whenever ocean salinity, atmospheric temperature, or gas composition exceeded certain limits.

Biological systems heavily rely on negative feedback to function correctly. When our body lacks oxygen, brainstem neurons cause our breathing to quicken. When we have too much oxygen (e.g., from hyperventilating), the same neurons slow our breathing. If the salt concentration in our blood exceeds healthy levels, osmoreceptors in our hypothalamus activate, motivating us to drink fluids to restore the salt concentration. When we're cold, other sensors in our hypothalamus turn on, causing us to shiver and generate heat from muscle contractions. When we get too hot, we sweat to shed excess heat.

Aware that all living organisms rely on such negative feedback mechanisms to survive, Lovelock began to suspect that biology—not physics, chemistry, or geology—held the keys to understanding why conditions on Earth have remained constant over billions of years.

Just as our bodies have negative feedback loops that keep oxygen, salt, and temperature within healthy limits, Lovelock reasoned that biological forces might somehow act on sky, land, and oceans to keep oxygen, salt, and temperature within healthy ranges for living organisms.

As he explored the concept, Lovelock discovered multiple ways that life on Earth, acting as a single entity, might keep conditions within the "Goldilocks" zone where life can thrive.

- Bacteria along shorelines can cause limestone to form and seal off salt lagoons that, through evaporation and sedimentation, remove salt from the ocean. And seabirds eat salt-containing marine life, depositing salt-bearing waste onto the land.

- When temperatures rise, ocean algae proliferate. These algae secrete sulfur-bearing aerosols that seed cloud formation, leading to increased sunlight's reflection into space and cooling the planet.

- Suppose the percentage of oxygen in the atmosphere increases to unhealthy levels (many organisms can't tolerate high oxygen levels, and too much oxygen can cause the atmosphere to ignite from lightning strikes). In that case, zooplankton and other microorganisms increase their oxygen consumption, releasing carbon compounds (such as methane) that react with oxygen to reduce its concentration. Increased oxygen also may cause more forest fires, which consume lots of oxygen.

These discoveries led Lovelock to formulate the "Gaia hypothesis," which argues that all life on the planet acts in concert through negative feedback loops to keep environmental conditions optimized for life (in Greek mythology, Gaia was a goddess who personified Earth).

Gaia, in Lovelock's formulation, is not necessarily a sentient being. Still, it has characteristics of intelligence in that it senses threats to its welfare and changes its behavior to reduce those threats.

All of this happens because different living organisms—even those of radically different species— do interact in many ways. Here is a short list of symbiotic interdependencies among different life forms on Earth:

- Trees in a forest warn each other of bug damage through pheromone release.
- Bees pollinate crops.

- Herbivores, and the plants they eat evolve into an equilibrium where enough plants survive to feed future generations of herbivores, but the herbivores do not over graze, killing off their food source.
- Plants produce oxygen that allows animals to breathe, and animals repay the favor by exhaling carbon dioxide that plants need to survive.
- Animals eat and spread the seeds of many plants.
- Prey and predators who hunt them evolve into equilibrium conditions where there are just the right number of both prey and predators to ensure neither goes extinct.

Dr Frank and colleagues go further, postulating that humans, with all their knowledge and technology, and other living entities, comprise a collective emergent planetary intelligence.

Is that intelligence –if it indeed exists–superior to that of the most intelligent humans, in the same way, an entire brain is more intelligent than the individual neurons that make it up?

And could such an intelligence, for reasons we couldn't begin to fathom (in the same way a single neuron couldn't see the bigger picture of what the brain it's in is doing), be responsible for UFOs?

Atmospheric scientists such as Lovelock have already gone so far as to assert that the planet can "decide" to change its' own climate: Could the planet use such "powers" to form -for example-lightning that behaves like a UFO when it so chooses?

So here, at last, we've added a new alternative to the exhaustive list of UFO possibilities: That a non-human intelligence (the Earth itself) sometimes intentionally harnesses natural phenomena to "fake UFOs."

Why would a super-intelligence do such a thing?

President Ronald Reagan gave us a hint when he said: *"Perhaps we need some outside universal threat to make us recognize this common bond. I occasionally think how quickly our differences worldwide would vanish if we faced an alien threat from outside this world."*

Perhaps the living Earth is getting anxious over the possibility that it will die in an all-out nuclear exchange if antagonism among humans continues unabated, and it's adopted the Ronald Reagan idea of unifying humans with the common threat of ETs.

If we've lost you at this point by crossing the boundaries of your comfort zone, that was our intent. The intelligent planet hypothesis for UFOs is very unlikely to be true. But something equally weird probably *is* true: Undiscovered atmospheric effects, strange physics, ETs, you name it. We don't know enough to give you the ultimate truth, but this example gives an idea of what the truth will probably *feel* like when we finally learn it.

Our motivation for venturing into the discomfort zone of science goes back to the reason we started the book by talking about human perception, cognition and motivation. The reason we haven't solved the UFO mystery in 80 years may reveal more about us, and our limitations, than UFOs. Thus, acknowledging and confronting those limitations could ultimately be more helpful in getting to the truth than confining our efforts to gathering more data, because the truth may live in our discomfort zone.

That said, we'll now dive even deeper into the discomfort zone by talking about ETs.

Thoughts on ETs

Notice from the preceding discussion—and our earlier dive into time travel—that "non-human" does not necessarily equate to ETs.

But suppose for a moment that UFOs are products of honest-to-God ETs from planet X in Galaxy Y. What can we say about them that hasn't already surfaced in zillions of other places?

That's tough, but we'll try adding new ideas to the crowded field.

One idea is the probability that UFOs are—how can we say it-*un-aliened*? For all the same reasons that any human-made UFOs with ungodly accelerations are probably unmanned, the UFOs pulling jaw-dropping Gs could have no living organisms inside them, depending on your definition of "living organism."

Could a sufficiently advanced AI that steered a UFO be considered alive? It's hard to say, especially if that AI had some semblance of consciousness and had "emotions."

But whether hardware, software, and other kinds of high tech that ETs might cram into UFOs, it's unlikely that they are biological, especially considering the rigors of space travel to get here.

If ETs even remotely resemble humans, intense radiation in space, weightlessness, and limited life spans for very long trips would likely limit the options for interstellar travel in person, as it were, although it's always possible that suspended animation, long life spans, counter radiation measures, etc., not to mention faster than light travel through distorted spacetime could change all that.

But, playing the odds as we now understand them, if ETs created UFOs, they are most likely automated probes like the ones we have sent into space.

Again, we must take great care not to anthropomorphize other species, especially those from other planets.

Just as all life forms on Earth evolved to thrive in specific ecological niches, maybe the environmental niche that some ETs evolved in was outer space.

Going back to the idea that the universe is ancient, and other species could thus have gotten a few million-year evolutionary head start on us, it's not all that far-fetched to suppose another species evolved with very long lifespans, natural suspended animation (akin to hibernation seen on Earth, but much longer), and an ability to thrive in weightlessness and high radiation.

From the existence of extremophiles on our planet, some of which can survive the radiation and vacuum of space, we have proof that such things might be possible.

As Michael Crichton observed in *Jurassic Park*, life always finds a way.

Has it found its way here?

Panspermia and evidence that ETs have already arrived

Bees pollinate plants and the wind spreads seeds, so some scientists speculate that, in the same manner, asteroids and comets seed life across the universe.

A meteorite discovered in Antarctica, determined to be ejected from Mars, probably after a big meteorite collision, bore marks that a few scientists interpret as fossils of bacterial colonies.

Whether or not ancient life on Mars made its way here in fossil form, the controversy surrounding it, together with discoveries of extremophiles (and tardigrades) surviving the harshness of space (researchers found living organisms on the surface of the space shuttle in orbit), raise the possibility that life on Earth itself initially rode here from somewhere else: Not all life, but some forms of life. This theory, called Panspermia, is favored by some scientists based upon the rapid emergence of life on Earth less than a billion years after the planet formed.

Mathematical analysis of the "molecular clock" in DNA (e.g., how many DNA replications since the original molecule) and radioisotope studies hinting at biogenic sources of some chemicals in rocks suggest that life may have sprung up here a mere 500 million years after the Earth formed, but not more than 1 billion after the event. Some scientists believe this is too short for something as complex as life to evolve (3,4,5).

The Panspermia theory is far from widely accepted, but it's one of those theories, like wormholes, that some reputable scientists believe is not impossible.

If the Panspermia hypothesis turns out to be true, and life evolved on Earth from organisms that originally sprang up elsewhere, there are two big implications:

First, ETs (if microorganisms qualify as ETs) have come here, and we are all their descendants.

Second, ET organisms evolved here on Earth into an intelligent species that wants to explore the cosmos. So, if Panspermia theory is true, we have proof that ET organisms *can* evolve into species that can dream of space travel. Which means that our distant relatives elsewhere in the cosmos, could also have evolved intelligence, and along with it, their own dreams of reaching distant stars.

And the only difference between us and those far distant cousins might be that we can still only dream about what our cousins have already achieved.

Conclusion

Analysts in DOD, NASA, and the Intelligence Community are unlikely to issue assessments that point to ETs as the only viable explanation for unexplained UFOs, even if those analysts, deep down, believe it.

And those analysts would have excellent reasons for showing restraint because more definitive assessments wouldn't change made-up minds, and all the analysts would accomplish would be to attract ridicule and be replaced by more circumspect, politically astute analysts. The ET alternative simply lives too deep inside the Government discomfort zone.

But we are not cautious, politically astute Government analysts, so we will venture out on a limb with the following:

We assess that:

1) UFOs almost certainly represent multiple, unrelated phenomena, most of which arise from human activity, natural phenomena, and human perception, cognition, and observer judgment errors.

2) A few UFO reports are unlikely to arise from human activity, natural phenomena, or human perception, cognition, and judgment errors. Therefore, we assess that a small percentage of UFO reports arise from exotic phenomena unknown to current science.

"Unknown to current science" does not equate to ETs, as we pointed out earlier, but it could mean ETs. Or it could mean that investigating UFOs will unravel important unanswered science questions about the brain, the universe, the atmosphere, or physics.

One way or another, though, UFOs could well turn out to be a turning point in human history, where there was "before" we discovered the answer(s) and after we discovered them.

And, as two scientists getting on in years, we hope "after" comes sooner than later.

References

1) Geophysiology, the science of Gaia - Lovelock - 1989 - Reviews of Geophysics - Wiley Online Library

2) Intelligence as a planetary scale process | International Journal of Astrobiology | Cambridge Core

3) **Genome increase as a clock for the origin and evolution of life | Biology Direct | Full Text (biomedcentral.com)**

4) GTOs and HGT: genes are older than expected and can be installed by horizontal gene transfer, especially with help from viruses (spiedigitallibrary.org)

5) [1304.3381] Life Before Earth (arxiv.org)

Acknowledgements

We thank Dr. Alan Chodos for feedback on physics questions and drone expert Cliff Wong for ideas about faking UFOs. Any errors in those topics are our fault, not Alan or Cliff's.

DALL-E 3 from Open AI rendered the artist's concepts throughout the book and the cover art.

About the authors

Dr. Eric Haseltine was Director of Research at NSA and Associate Director of National Intelligence, in charge of Science and Technology for the US Intelligence Community. Prior to joining the Government, Eric was Executive Vice President of Walt Disney Imagineering, in charge of R&D for the corporation. He is a neuroscientist who has written hundreds of popular science articles on the brain for Discover Magazine and Psychology Today, and a named inventor on 70 patents in the fields of optics, special effects and magnetometry. He has authored multiple books on innovation and the brain as well as a true spy thriller, *The Spy in Moscow Station*. Dr. Haseltine currently serves as Chairman of the US Technology Leadership council.

Dr. Chris Gilbert is an MD physician with a PhD in physiology, who has written extensively on her pioneering techniques in mind-body medicine, including the widely acclaimed *The Listening Cure*. A frequent co-author with her husband Eric Haseltine, she has written over a hundred articles for PsychologyToday.com. A long-time member of Doctors Without Borders, SAG actress and radio personality, Dr. Gilbert is much sought-after on the speaking circuit. She currently serves as President of Discovery Democracy LLC., a high-tech start up that makes and sells magnetic sensors.